$1·75

A TREASURY OF AUSTRALIAN WILDFLOWERS

Douglass Baglin, Barbara Mullins and Frank Hurley

URE SMITH • SYDNEY
in association with
MULAVON PTY LTD • SYDNEY

This edition first published in Australia 1972
by Ure Smith Pty Ltd, 176 South Creek Road,
Dee Why West 2099 and
Mulavon Pty Ltd, 70 Haigh Avenue, Belrose 2085

National Library of Australia Card
Number and ISBN 0 7254 0095 1
Designed by Beryl Green
Printed in Singapore by Toppan
Printing Company (S) Private Limited

The four titles in this edition *Australian Eucalypts* (1966), *Australia's Wildflowers* (1968), *Australian Wattles* (1968) and *Australian Banksias* (1970) were first published in The Australian Heritage Series by Horwitz Publications (now published by Mulavon Pty Ltd)

Other titles available in The Heritage Series:

Captain Cook's Australia
Aborigines of Australia
Australia's Great Barrier Reef
Australia's Northern Territory
Kosciusko National Park
Australian Eucalypts
Canberra on the Monaro
Ku-ring-gai Chase National Park
Australia's Hunter River Valley
Aboriginal Art of Australia

CONTENTS

ILLUSTRATIONS

AUSTRALIA'S WILDFLOWERS (photographs by Frank Hurley)

AUSTRALIAN WATTLES (photographs by Douglass Baglin)

AUSTRALIAN EUCALYPTS (photographs by Douglass Baglin)

AUSTRALIAN BANKSIA (photographs by Douglass Baglin)

ACKNOWLEDGEMENTS

The authors extend sincere thanks to the Director and staff of the National Herbarium of New South Wales, the Curator and staff of the Western Australian Herbarium, Mr. J. H. Willis, Assistant Government Botanist, Victoria, Dr. H. J. Eichler, Keeper of the State Herbarium, South Australia and Mr. L. L. Pedley of the Queensland Herbarium for their help in the identification of photographs, and also for permission to use the research facilities of the National Herbarium Library. Also acknowledged with gratitude is considerable assistance from Dr. Mary Tindale (acacias), Mr. L. A. S. Johnson (eucalypts), Mr. D. McGillivary and Mr. D. Blaxell (banksias).

INTRODUCTION

Australia, last frontier for the exploration and discovery of new plants, is a floral wonderland for botanists and garden lovers alike. In this vast continent of varied climates and soils, much of the flora is unique and all is beautiful.

The winter snows of the southern tablelands are replaced in summer by a mantle of alpine flowers. Following even the lightest shower of rain, the barren desert lands spring to life almost overnight, and the flat plains are covered as far as the eye can see with every conceivable colour. In the rainforests of Queensland are trees not yet described, though the area is known to abound with plants of great beauty, as well as some with valuable medicinal properties. Sandy heathlands and stony deserts have produced native plants which have learned to cope with harsh environments or perish: four thousand million years of natural selection have found a myriad of answers to drought and heat which may yet solve problems of survival and sustain the life of mankind. The Hawkesbury sandstone country of coastal New South Wales contains a greater variety of plants than the whole of the British Isles, and many are confined to this limited area. The southwest corner of Western Australia, isolated by sea and sand for countless centuries and probably the most ancient land mass on the face of the earth, has developed a specialised flora of remarkable beauty.

This is our treasury of wildflowers. It is threatened by urban and rural development, by mining on coastal beaches, tropical rainforests and arid inland plains. Its wealth is still unknown and, unlike our mineral resources, it is a treasure which can be used again and again—provided we do not destroy it. It is part of Australia's heritage, the preservation of which this book, like the series from which the four separate titles are reprinted, is dedicated.

Barbara Mullins

The glorious gold of wattle against the blue of Australian skies is a trademark throughout the continent. There are over 600 indigenous species, and they form the largest genus in the flora of this land, occurring in infinite variety, size and flowering season, from rich coastal regions to inland deserts, in some cases inhabiting regions where even the eucalypt cannot maintain an existence.

One of the most spectacular is the COOTAMUNDRA WATTLE (*Acacia baileyana*) pictured below. In nature confined to a few localities on the western slopes of New South Wales, this is now known and cultivated throughout the world. It is a fast-growing small tree, with feathery, silver-grey foliage, and carries a profusion of fluffy golden flowers in winter and early spring.

▽ ACACIA BAILEYANA

PATERSONIA SERICEA △

NYMPHAEA SPECIES △

PURPLE FLAG (*Patersonia sericea*). The flowers of this delicate native iris have three fragile petals and are enclosed in a hairy sheathing bract. Though each individual flower soon fades, it is quickly replaced by another.

BLUE WATERLILY (*Nymphaea* species). This native waterlily has large flowers, up to ten inches across, carried on long stalks, well above the water. Its range extends from northern N.S.W. through tropical Australia to southern New Guinea.

EPACRIS MICROPHYLLA △

△ RICINOCARPOS PINIFOLIUS

The long snowy-white spikes are the CORAL HEATH (*Epacris microphylla*), a prickly little shrub found on sandy and swampy areas of coastal N.S.W. and Queensland. It blooms profusely in winter and early spring. The open, five-petalled flowers belong to the WHITE WEDDING BUSH (*Ricinocarpos pinifolius*) a small and shapely shrub of sandy coastal areas of eastern Australia. Blooms are up to an inch across, and are carried in massed clusters.

STENOCARPUS SINUATUS △

▽ HIBBERTIA SPECIES

CHORIZEMA CORDATUM △

△ OLEARIA TOMENTOSA

Top, left: The flowers of the FIREWHEEL TREE (*Stenocarpus sinuatus*) are bright red, wheel-shaped, and grow as large as four inches in diameter. This tree grows 40 to 50 feet high and occurs in coastal rainforest gullies of New South Wales and Queensland.

Far left: The HEART LEAF FLAME PEA (*Chorizema cordatum*) commences blooming in winter and carries its profusion of brilliant orange-red flowers throughout spring. This hardy dwarf shrub is a native of Western Australia.

GUINEA FLOWERS (*Hibbertia* species) left, are widespread throughout Australia, particularly in coastal regions. The bright yellow, open flowers of the species pictured make a spectacular display in winter and early spring.

Above: DAISY BUSH (*Olearia tomentosa*) has large flower heads, up to two inches across, ranging in colour from white to blue or pink. It is a native of coastal New South Wales.

West Australia's fantastic CHRISTMAS TREE (*Nuytsia floribunda*), below, belongs to the parasitic mistletoe family, but, unlike mistletoe, is attached to the roots of the host plant.

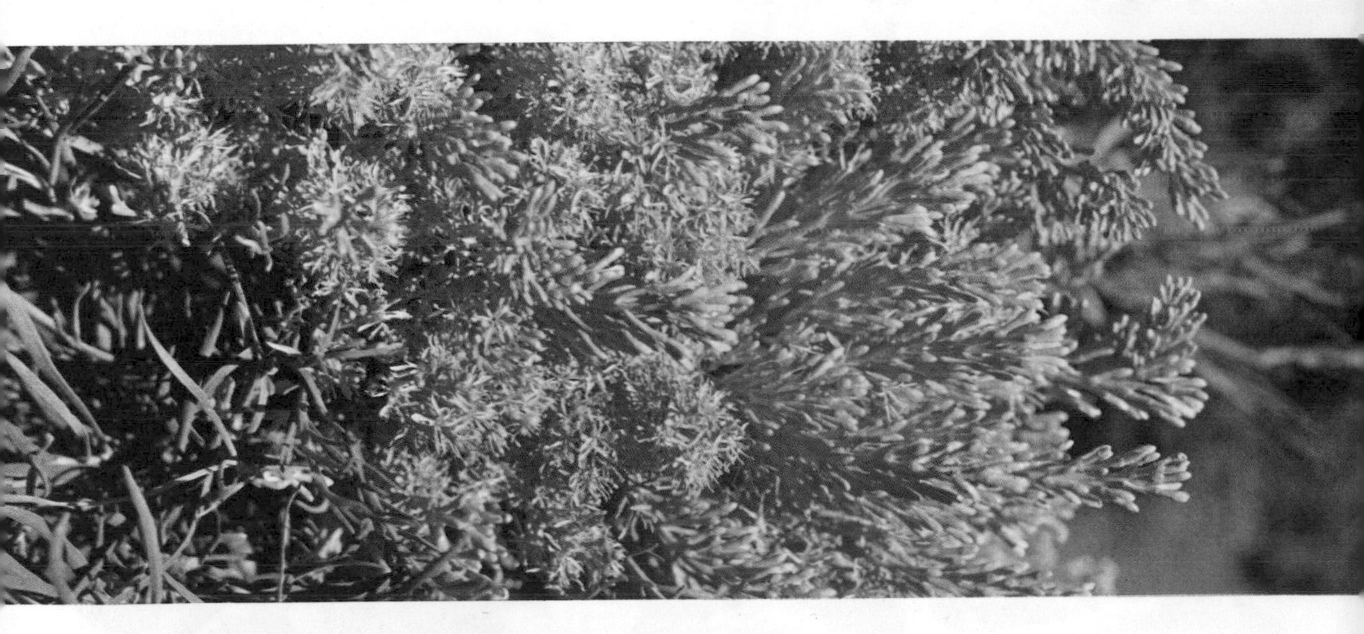

Pictured below is *Pittosporum revolutum*, a small to medium-sized tree of coastal eastern Australia. The creamy-yellow flowers are small, but the inch-long orange-coloured fruit, which splits to reveal bright-red, sticky seeds, is most spectacular and attractive to birds. Young twigs and undersurfaces of the large, dark green leaves are covered with fine, rust-coloured hairs.

PITTOSPORUM REVOLUTUM ▽

△ TETRATHECA SPECIES

The BLACK-EYED SUSAN (*Tetratheca* species) belongs to a plant family unique to Australia. There are about twenty species of these little, heath-like, wiry shrubs, and the common name of the one pictured refers to the deeply coloured anthers which are clustered together in the centre of the flower.

More than half the Tetrathecas are confined to West Australia, and the remaining species are scattered throughout the eastern states. The bell-like flowers, up to an inch across, vary in colour from pale pink to purple, and are usually carried in great profusion.

CHRISTMAS BELLS (*Blandfordia nobilis*), left, are lily-like plants which carry their waxy, bell-shaped flowers in summer. The species pictured is confined to New South Wales, and it is very common in sandy and swampy situations there.

There are three species of *Blandfordia,* all of which have red and yellow bells borne in clusters on the end of erect stems rising from the centre of a tuft of grass-like leaves. *B. grandiflora* has larger, deeper red flowers than *B. nobilis* and is endemic to the sandstone crags of the Blue Mountains; *B. flammea* occurs in northern New South Wales and southern Queensland, and *B. marginata,* perhaps the loveliest of them all, is confined to Tasmania, where it is often known as the Gordon River Lily.

◁ BLANDFORDIA NOBILIS

△ DORYANTHES EXCELSA

The GYMEA LILY (*Doryanthes excelsa*) also known as the Giant Lily, grows to 15 feet high and bears a dense globular head of spectacular red fleshy flowers, as large as a cabbage. This flowerhead is carried on the end of a long thick stem, arising from a cluster of giant leaves, three or four feet long and most decorative in their own right. It is found in coastal areas of New South Wales th Wales to Queensland.

The RIVER ROSE (*Bauera rubioides*) pictured lower left, is a little, wiry, profusely flowering shrub which haunts moist places and creek banks in eastern Australia, often forming dense, almost impenetrable clumps. It flowers from spring to late summer.

△ HIBBERTIA SPECIES

Above is another species of *Hibbertia*, the GUINEA FLOWER (see also page 6). These gay-coloured flowers are found in all states of Australia. Some are scrambling shrubs, and some, like the species pictured, are erect. They bloom in winter and spring.

The TASMANIAN WARATAH (*Telopea truncata*) is shown opposite with the white-flowered *Richea dracophylla*, also a native of the island state.

BAUERA RUBIOIDES ▷

The genus *Pimelea* is confined to Australia and New Zealand, but belongs to the same family as the well-known garden plant, Daphne. There are about eighty *Pimelea* species, well-distributed throughout all states, but particularly well represented in Western Australia. The species pictured is probably *Pimelea suaveolens,* a native of the west.

Tasmanian mountain berries from the Mount Wellington district. The white fruits are the SNOW BERRY (*Gaultheria hispida*), the red fruits are the PINK MOUNTAIN BERRY (*Cyathodes parvifolia*) and the purple are the BLUE MOUNTAIN BERRY (*Billardiera longiflora*). Pictured below is *Pittosporum undulatum,* the MOCK ORANGE, which is a native of eastern Australia and flowers in spring. Its scented white blossoms, citrus-like leaves and small, bright orange fruit have led to its common name. Shown in the lower picture is the West Australian ENAMEL ORCHID (*Glossodia emarginata*).

△ TASMANIAN MOUNTAIN BERRIES

△ PITTOSPORUM UNDULATUM

▽ GLOSSODIA EMARGINATA

△ ANGOPHORA CORDIFOLIA

The DWARF APPLE (*Angophora cordifolia*) is prevalent in the Hawkesbury sandstone area of coastal New South Wales. It is a low spreading shrub with rough bark, and in summer is covered with masses of sweet-smelling creamy-white flowers up to an inch across. *Angophora* blooms closely resemble those of the Eucalypts, and indeed the genera are closely related. They can be distinguished by the absence, in the Angophoras, of the operculum or cap on the flowerbud, a characteristic of the Eucalypts, and by the five-ribbed calyx, typical of the Angophoras. Also, all *Angophora* species have opposite leaves.

STURT'S DESERT PEA (*Clianthus formosus*), below, is a desert flower occurring naturally in the arid interior. One of the most brilliant and beautiful of all Australian natives, it is South Australia's official floral emblem. The glossy red and black blooms are up to four inches long, and hang in clusters on short, erect stems.

△ CLIANTHUS FORMOSUS

DENDROBIUM SPECIOSUM ▷

The ROCK LILY (*Dendrobium speciosum*), is not a lily at all, but one of Australia's indigenous orchids. It is epiphytic, growing on rocks or trees in eastern N.S.W. and Queensland, and carries its golden, creamy or pure white fragrant blossom in long spikes, often containing hundreds of individual blooms.

△ EUCALYPTUS MACROCARPA

ANIGOZANTHOS MANGLESII △

The MOTTLECAH (*Eucalyptus macrocarpa*), above left, is also called Desert Pride and Rose-of-the-West. Its spectacular, gold-tipped blossom grows up to three to five inches in diameter, and is the largest of the Eucalypts. The tree itself is small and often straggly in habit, but the stem-clasping, silvery-blue foliage is attractive and the blossoms are carried for nine months of the year. The Mottlecah is a native of West Australia.

The KANGAROO PAW (*Anigozanthos manglesii*), above right, is the floral emblem of West Australia. These quaint, unusually-coloured flowers are covered with a soft downy wool, and the bright red of the base of the flower extends down the long flowering stem. There are several species of kangaroo paws, all confined in nature to West Australia.

The COOKTOWN ORCHID (*Dendrobium bigibbum*), below, is an epiphytic orchid found on trees in northern Queensland, and is that state's floral emblem. The pink blooms are often two inches or more across, and are carried profusely on long sprays.

▽ DENDROBIUM BIGIBBUM

△ LESCHENAULTIA MACRANTHA

▽ EPACRIS IMPRESSA

The COMMON HEATH (*Epacris impressa*), left, has a colour range from white through various shades of pink to deep red. It is common in sandy and swampy areas of southern New South Wales, Victoria, Tasmania and South Australia, and is Victoria's official floral emblem.

The ACORN BANKSIA (*Banksia prionotes*), below, is a West Australian species with bright orange flower spikes, three to five inches long, and contrasting woolly grey buds. When the spikes are half-open, as pictured, they have an attractive, acorn-like appearance. The narrow leaves are up to a foot long.

BANKSIA PRIONOTES ▽

The glowing orange flowers pictured at top, opposite, are those of *Leschenaultia macrantha,* the largest-flowered of the Leschenaultias. The bush itself is mat-like, rarely more than a few inches high, though it may spread over an area of two or three feet.

WILD COTTON TREE △

The WILD COTTON TREE (*Cochlospermum fraseri*), left, is a native of the Northern Territory. In the flowering season it is covered with large, showy yellow flowers, and the seed, within its protective capsule, is encased in soft, cotton-like down, hence the common name.

ACETOSA VESICARIA ▽ SOLANUM SPECIES

DISPHYMA AUSTRALE ▽

△ HELIPTERUM SPECIES

When the rains fall in the arid heart of Australia, the desert blooms. The bare red sands and stony wastes which seemed utterly devoid of life only a week or so before are covered with an unbelievable profusion of colourful flowers. Shown at far left is the rosy WILD HOPS (*Acetosa vesicaria*), not a native of Australia but now naturalized and a feature in the inland. The purple flower is a species of *Solanum,* and the white EVERLASTING DAISIES (centre) are a species of *Helipterum*. The mauve succulent pictured below, left, is a NATIVE PIG-FACE (*Disphyma australe*), which grows and flourishes on the shores of inland salt-pans. Below is the remarkable WREATH LESCHENAULTIA. This low-growing shrub develops its flowers around its periphery, forming a colourful ring up to three feet in diameter. Areas in flower resemble a mass burial ground, covered with wreaths.

Various are the ways in which the desert plants adapt themselves to their harsh environment. The ephemerals evade rather than resist the drought. These are the flowering annuals, such as daisies, the seeds of which lie dormant during the dry period. After rain they germinate, flower, set seed and die, all within a few short weeks, during which the desert is literally carpeted with vibrant colour. Perennial plants often survive because of underground food storage in the form of bulbs, tubers or rhizomes; they die right back

LESCHENAULTIA SPECIES △

BRACHYCOME SPECIES PTILOTUS SPECIES TRICHODESMA ZEYLANICUM △

or reduce themselves to a framework of bare branches in the dry season, and produce rapidly flowering shoots after rain. Succulents store water in thick fleshy stems or leaves, xeromorphs feature greatly reduced and protected leaf structures which limit loss of moisture.

Below: Giant waterlilies, such as *Nymphaea stellata*, grow in profusion on the lagoons of the Northern Territory. Their starchy tubers form a useful food item for nomadic aborigines, and the seed will withstand prolonged periods of drought.

Above: NATIVE DAISIES, probably *Brachycome* species, with papery EVERLASTINGS (*Helipterum* species), mauve FEATHERHEADS (*Ptilotus* species) and the blue flowers of *Trichodesma zeylanicum*, which the aborigines call "rodinga" and the cattlemen of the inland "cattle-bush", because of its usefulness as a desert fodder.

▽ NYMPHAEA STELLATA

PINK BUTTONS (*Kunzea capitata*) grows in moist, peaty soils along the coast of eastern Australia, from Victoria to northern New South Wales. It carries a profusion of rosy pink, pom-pom flower-clusters in spring and summer. Kunzeas are found only in Australia, and are closely related to the tea trees (*Leptospermum*).

GUM BLOSSOM (*Eucalyptus* species) is a feature of the Australian bush. There are over 400 eucalypts, ranging from stunted desert mallees to the majestic Mountain Ash, the tallest hardwood in the world. Many species are valuable honey trees, a source of both nectar and pollen.

△ KUNZEA CAPITATA

EUCALYPTUS SPECIES ▽

CORREA REFLEXA △

NATIVE FUCHSIA (*Correa reflexa*), left, is a relative of the Boronias. It grows in sandy soil along the coast of eastern Australia, extending into the coastal dunes and acting as a sand-binder. The bell-shaped flowers are usually red with yellow tips, as in the specimen pictured, but some varieties are entirely green, yellowish-green, or even white.

The SILKY OAK (*Grevillea robusta*), below, is both a beautiful ornamental and a valuable timber tree. The brilliant orange flowers are carried in clusters in summer, and the oak-like timber is used in furniture and plywood. The largest of the Grevilleas, it grows from 25 to 100 feet high, and is a native of Queensland and New South Wales.

HONEY FLOWER (*Lambertia formosa*), right, is a relative of the Waratah. A stiff little shrub five or six feet high, it has bright red tubular flowers rich in nectar and attractive to honey-eating birds, and curious horned woody seed pods ("Mountain Devils"). It is a native of the coast and tablelands of New South Wales.

GREVILLEA ROBUSTA △

△ LAMBERTIA FORMOSA

△ TELOPEA SPECIOSISSIMA

CONOSTYLIS SPECIES ▽

WARATAH (*Telopea speciosissima*) is the official floral emblem of New South Wales. The showy, brilliant red flower-head is actually a collection of numerous individual flowers surrounded by colourful bracts, and the apt generic name is from the Greek *telopos*, meaning "seen from afar". In nature it has a limited range in coastal sandstone and tableland areas of New South Wales, but it is widely cultivated elsewhere in gardens.

▽ ISOPOGON DUBIUS

PINK CONEBUSH (*Isopogon dubius*), above, is a native of West Australia. A low shrub with prickly foliage, it flowers profusely in winter and early spring.

Another, unrelated West Australian is the WHITE CONEFLOWER (*Conostylis* species), shown left, a little tufted plant with grass-like foliage, closely allied to the Kangaroo Paws. As with the "paws", flowers and stems are covered with soft, downy wool.

Right: *Kunzea ambigua*, a common plant of coastal eastern Australia. This is a shrub to ten feet high, beloved of birds and bees for its nectar-laden blossoms. In spring it is a mass of densely-packed, honey-perfumed flowers, carried on long spikes and almost completely hiding the tiny, narrow leaves. In nature this kunzea often forms dense thickets, and in cultivation it makes an excellent background shrub.

▽ KUNZEA AMBIGUA

△ ACTINOTUS HELIANTHI

FLANNEL FLOWER (*Actinotus helianthi*), with its white, woolly, flannel-like bracts, is common along sandstone areas of coastal New South Wales and also extends into southern Queensland and Victoria. The "flower" consists of white, petal-like bracts surrounding a dense cluster of tiny florets, and the entire plant is coated with a soft, velvety down.

BANKSIA ATTENUATA ▽

Pictured on this page are three Banksias, members of the genus which commemorates the name of botanist Sir Joseph Banks. The one shown at left is *Banksia ericifolia*, first specimens of which were collected by Banks himself when a member of Cook's voyage of discovery in 1770. Commonly called Heath-leafed Honeysuckle, this is a small, dense, very shapely tree found mainly in Hawkesbury sandstone country of coastal New South Wales. Above is *Banksia attenuata*, a West Australian species, and below is *Banksia coccinea*, another West Australian, in company with golden Dryandras. Banksia flowers are carried in densely packed spikes or cones. They are rich in nectar, and many are important honey plants.

△ BANKSIA ERICIFOLIA

▽ BANKSIA COCCINEA

GREVILLEA PETROPHILOIDES △

▽ GREVILLEA EXCELSIOR

BLUEBERRY ASH (*Elaeocarpus reticulatus*), left, is a small tree from coastal eastern Australia. The attractive sprays of creamy white fringed flowers appear in spring, and are followed by bright blue berries. Foliage is dark glossy green when mature, pink to red when young, and the tree is shapely in habit, growing to 20 or more feet.

CURRAWONG (*Acacia doratoxylon*) is a small to medium-sized tree which occurs on the dry ridges of the central western slopes of New South Wales. This wattle flowers in spring, and is a valuable source of pollen for bees.

Grevilleas are a large group of Australian plants, mainly shrubs but including some trees, such as the Silky Oak pictured on page 22. Shown above left, is PINK SILK GREVILLEA (*Grevillea petrophiloides*), a shrub which grows to about four feet. A native of inland West Australia, it produces a profusion of pink flower spikes in spring. Below is the PINE GREVILLEA (*Grevillea excelsior*), also from the west. This is a small tree, growing to 20 feet, and the spectacular flower spikes form a colourful pyramid from the bright gold of fully-opened blossoms to silvery grey buds.

ACACIA DORATOXYLON ▷

DAMPIERA SPECIES △

BLUE DAMPIERA (above) belongs to the same plant family as the Leschenaultias. All of the 60 species in this genus are unique to Australia, and most are blue-flowered. The generic name *Dampiera* commemorates William Dampier, who collected the first specimens and remarked on the number of blue flowers occurring in New Holland.

GRAVEL BOTTLEBRUSH (*Beaufortia sparsa*) is a native of the south coast of West Australia. It grows to about 6 feet and carries its brilliant red flowers in summer.
The WATTLE pictured opposite is *Acacia parramattensis,* a native of new South Wales and common around Sydney and the lower Blue Mountains.

▽ BEAUFORTIA SPARSA

△ ERIOSTEMON LANCEOLATUS

PINK WAXFLOWER (*Eriostemon lanceolatus*) is a close relative of the Boronias. Its starry pink flowers are waxy in appearance and are carried in such profusion in spring and summer that the branches are often weighed down, giving the plant an attractive weeping habit. It is a native of coastal eastern Australia.

CRIMSON BOTTLEBRUSH (*Callistemon citrinus*) flowers in winter and spring. It is a stiff shrub, normally growing from five to 15 feet, and is widely cultivated in gardens. Like the *Eriostemon* above, it is a native of the east coast and is common in the Hawkesbury sandstone country around Sydney.

FRINGE VIOLET (*Thysanotus* species) flowers in spring and summer and is common in open grasslands. There are over 20 species of these attractive, delicately fringed flowers, most of them endemic to West Australia.

◁ CALLISTEMON CITRINUS

△ THYSANOTUS SPECIES

CALECTASIA CYNEA △

TINSEL LILY (*Calectasia cynea*) is an Australian member of the Lily family. Colour of the corolla and calyx ranges from a rich blue to a lustrous purple, contrasting spectacularly with prominent, orange-gold stamens. This flower is of the dry, "everlasting" type, and is commonly found on the sand-plains of West Australia, though it is also a feature in some parts of South Australia and western Victoria.

DRUMSTICKS (*Petrophile linearis*), below, is a small shrub from the sandy coastal areas of West Australia. The velvety flowers are pink with grey tips, and the common name refers to the quaint, rounded seed cones.

▽ PETROPHILE LINEARIS

▽ DRYANDRA NIVEA

DRYANDRA (*Dryandra nivea*), left, is sometimes called Honeycups. Dryandras are closely related to the Banksias and there are about fifty species, all confined to West Australia. The one pictured, with its large golden flower-heads and long narrow saw-toothed leaves, is a very popular subject for indoor decoration.

BANKS GREVILLEA (*Grevillea banksii*) is a tall shrub or small tree growing eight to 15 feet high, which blooms continucusly in the warmer months. The flowerheads are up to six inches long and the foliage is dense, greyish-green and much divided. A native of Queensland, it has been extensively cultivated in gardens, and some beautiful varieties have been developed.

GREVILLEA BANKS △

△ ACACIA CYANOPHYLLA

Wattles fall into two broad categories: those that retain true leaves (always bipinnate, or fern-like) and those with leaves reduced to phyllodes (flattened stalks performing the function of leaves, ranging from mere prickles to broad, leaf-like structures). Except for a few species in New Guinea and the Pacific Islands, phyllodinous wattles are confined to Australia; the group includes the majority of Australian wattles. All acacias have the feathery, bipinnate leaves as seedlings. The change to phyllodes usually occurs at an early stage.

Western Australia's Golden Wattle *(Acacia cyanophylla,* pictured on front cover) is shown at left growing in its natural habitat along the upper reaches of the Swan River. This shapely shrub or small tree grows to ten to 25 feet high. Deep yellow, almost orange flowerheads are borne in late spring, so abundantly that the branchlets often droop with their weight. Sickle-shaped phyllodes are up to six inches long. Drought-hardy and salt-tolerant, it thrives in sand and is a valuable and very ornamental tree for erosion control or planting in seaside suburbs.

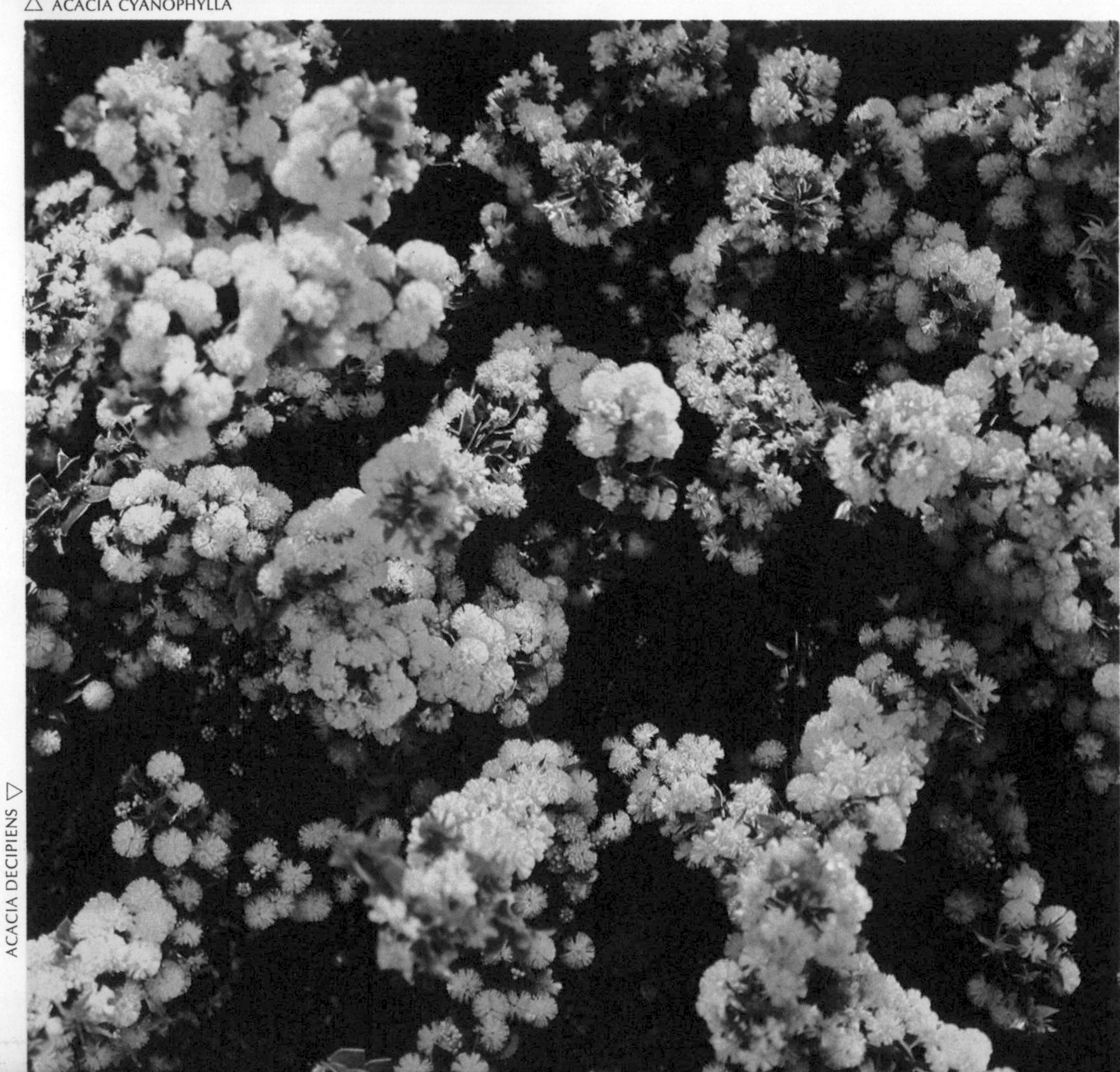

ACACIA DECIPIENS ▷

ACACIA UROPHYLLA ◁

ACACIA IMPLEXA ▽

Acacia urophylla (above), native to the south-west corner of Australia, is pictured here flowering in the Porongurup Ranges, near Albany, in company with purple Hovea and bracken fern. This is a prickly wattle, with pointed phyllodes and spiny stipules. Pale yellow flowerballs are borne profusely in spring. Phyllodes, up to three inches long and an inch broad, are curiously fluted along the upper margin, and have prominent net venation between the main veins. Pods are hard, very narrow, often twisted and coiled.

Acacia decipiens (left), another Western Australian wattle, is a low spreading shrub rarely higher than 18 inches or two feet. It has triangular, sharp-pointed phyllodes, about half an inch long. Deep yellow, fluffy flowerballs are borne singly in the axils in spring. This wattle grows in sandy places and is closely related to *Acacia cuneata*, pictured on page 15.

Acacia implexa (right) commonly called Hickory, is a small to medium-sized tree of temperate eastern Australia. Pale, delicately-perfumed flowerballs are borne in summer and autumn. Phyllodes, three to six inches long, many-veined and rather thin, taper to a point at the apex. Pods are long, narrow and twisted, with funicles folded under the seeds.

Acacia calamifolia (at right and below) is the Wallowa, a graceful widespreading shrub with slender branches and fine foliage, massed with large, bright yellow flowerballs from mid-winter to December. The needle-like phyllodes, two to four inches long, have a single vein, and are often hooked at the apex. Flowerballs are carried on short stalks, mostly in pairs. Wallowa prefers sandy soil or loam and endures dry conditions. A native of eastern States and South Australia, it grows six to 12 feet high.

Acacia melanoxylon (below) is the Blackwood, one of the largest of the acacias, a majestic tree sometimes reaching a height of a hundred feet or more in the rich soil of moist and sheltered mountain gullies. It is a valuable timber source, producing a golden to dark brown cabinet wood, often with an attractive fiddle-back figure. Masses of soft, pale yellow flowerballs are carried in winter and spring. Foliage is dense and dark green, with phyllodes many-veined and rounded at the apex. Pods, up to five inches long, are often twisted or curved into a circle; bright red funicles doubly enclose the seeds. Essentially a tree of the tablelands of eastern and southern Australia, the Blackwood also extends to coastal plains and western slopes.

△ ACACIA CALAMIFOLIA ▽

ACACIA MELANOXYLON ◁

ACACIA LINIFOLIA ▽

△ ACACIA ROSTELLIFERA

Acacia rostellifera (above) is a Western Australian wattle with willow-like habit. It grows ten to 15 feet high and the phyllodes, two to five inches long, are one-nerved, with prominent mid-rib. The flowering season extends from June to November, and the specimen pictured was photographed in late spring at Esperance Bay, on the south-west coast.

Acacia linifolia (left) is the Flax Wattle, a graceful, slender-branched shrub native to the coast and tablelands of New South Wales and Queensland. Pale flowerballs are borne in profusion on slender branches in late summer, autumn and winter. Phyllodes are about an inch or so long, smooth, dark green, and narrow.

The thorny wattle at right is *Acacia acutata,* shown growing in almost pure sand at Bonnie Rock in ancient Yilgarnia, Australia's oldest land mass. This tough little acacia carries scented, pale-yellow flowerballs in late winter and spring; it is confined to Western Australia.

ACACIA ACUTATA ▽

△ ACACIA HIPPUROIDES

At left is *Acacia hippuroides,* a prickly wattle, native to the tropics in Queensland, Northern Territory and Western Australia. This low, spreading shrub grows two to six feet high, and is usually found near watercourses. It is pictured here flowering in October on Cockatoo Island in Yampi Sound, off the north-west coast of Australia. The distinctively grooved phyllodes, about half an inch long, taper to a fine needle point, and are carried in whorls around the stem. Large, pale gold flowerballs are borne singly on long stalks. The bright green pods turn jet black when mature.

Often seen along the sandy or muddy sea-coast of north-western Australia is *Acacia sclerosperma,* pictured below growing in the sand dunes of Peron Peninsula, an area of cyclones and hurricanes; it is also common on red soil in the Gascoyne River area, where it often grows to a small tree. Phyllodes, up to four inches long, narrow,

ACACIA SCLEROSPERMA ▷

ACACIA ADUNCA △

rounded and one-veined, vary in colour from light green to blue-grey. Flowerheads are deep yellow, and the flowering season extends from April to December. Pods are woody and much-constricted, like a string of beads.

Acacia adunca (above) is a tall shrub or small tree, native to the tablelands of southern Queensland and northern New South Wales, as well as the central western slopes of the latter State. Phyllodes are long and very narrow. Rich golden flowerballs are borne in racemes in spring.

Acacia myrtifolia, shown below and at right, is the Myrtle-leafed Wattle, a shrubby acacia of upright angular habit found in all parts of the Commonwealth except the Northern Territory. Fluffy, pale yellow flowerheads are carried in winter and spring, and the one-ribbed phyllodes resemble gum leaves, particularly when the stems and young foliage are rosy-tinted, as is often the case. This hardy little shrub grows profusely in poor, rocky situations and is very common in the sandstone areas of eastern Australia, carpeting the inhospitable hillsides with soft colour, as shown below (photographed in the Dandenongs, Victoria).

△ ACACIA MYRTIFOLIA ▷

△ ACACIA BOORMANII ▽

The wattle pictured on these pages is *Acacia boormanii* (formerly *A. hunterana),* which has a limited range, chiefly along the deep valley of the Snowy River though there are a few isolated colonies elsewhere on the tablelands of New South Wales. A slender-branched shrub, three to ten feet high, it suckers profusely and young shoots have a silvery sheen. Phyllodes are soft, linear, one-veined, with a bent, sometimes hooked, apex. Racemes of bright yellow flowerballs are carried in profusion in early spring, clothing the steep mountain slopes in burnished gold. *A. boormanii* is pictured opposite, flowering in August in Kosciusko National Park, framing the lower reaches of the Snowy River.

The generic name *Acacia* is derived from the Greek "ake" a point ("akakia" is the name of some prickly species growing in Egypt). "Wattle", the common name widely applied in Australia, dates back to Anglo-Saxon times; it is a term for any flexible twigs interwoven to form a shelter. Early settlers in Australia used this technique to build walls of dwellings, sealing them with wet clay (hence "wattle and daub"). Strangely enough, originally the tree mostly used for this purpose was not an *Acacia,* but *Callicoma serratifolia,* then and now popularly known as Black Wattle.

△ ACACIA SCIRPIFOLIA ▽

The slender-foliaged *Acacia scirpifolia* (left) is a native of south-western Western Australia. Narrow, terete phyllodes are up to five inches long, and the small solitary flowerballs are carried in the axils. Pods are long, straight or almost so, and much contracted between the seeds. A bushy, erect shrub, six to 15 feet high, it flowers in spring and grows in sandy soil.

Acacia amoena (below) is a shapely wattle of the eastern Australian tablelands. A hardy shrub, often found in rocky situations, it has dark green phyllodes (with two to four marginal glands) and carries a profusion of bright golden flowerheads in spring. The specimen pictured was photographed on the slopes of Mount Kosciusko.

ACACIA AMOENA ▷

The unusual leafless wattle below is *Acacia alata*. Phyllodes are reduced to mere prickles, and flattened winged stems perform the function of leaves. Large, fluffy, pale yellow flowerballs appear along the bare stems in winter and early spring. This low-growing shrub is confined to the south-west corner of the continent, and is usually found in moist, shady situations. It is pictured here growing in the shade of huge eucalypts near Pemberton, W.A. In contrast the sickle-shaped phyllodes of *Acacia falcata* (right) are six or more inches long and up to an inch wide. A tough, hardy shrub, common on the temperate east coast, it grows to about ten feet. Pale lemon-yellow flowers are borne in clusters along reddish stems in winter.

△ ACACIA ALATA ▽

ACACIA FALCATA △

ACACIA ECHINULA △

The prickly wattle (above) is *Acacia echinula,* a wiry little shrub with sharp, pointed, thorn-like phyllodes. A native of the east coast and tablelands, it flourishes on sandstone in fairly exposed situations, and in spring is crowded with bright yellow flowerheads. It is very common in the Blue Mountains and Colo Heights district of New South Wales.

Below, left, is *Acacia armata,* the Kangaroo Thorn. The sharp spikes to which this tall prickly wattle owes its common name are modified stipules, carried in pairs at the base of oblong, wavy phyllodes. Large, dense, deep yellow flowerballs are borne in spring. *A. armata* can be found in temperate regions of all mainland states.

ACACIA CUNEATA ▽

Acacia cuneata is a glorious little wattle capable of growing in the most exposed and barren situations. It is pictured (below, left) growing in company with *Pimelea ferruginea* in almost pure sand on remote, windswept Cape Leeuwin, and (above) on the rocky sea coast of Flinders Bay.

Confined to south-western Australia, it is shown (below) with other hardy plants in the pebbly sand of this exposed corner of the continent. *A. cuneata* grows to two feet high. Phyllodes are an inverted wedge-shape, with a single vein, more central than in the closely-related *Acacia decipiens* (pictured page 4).

◁ ACACIA CUNEATA ▽

△ ACACIA UNDULIFOLIA

ACACIA SUAVEOLENS ▽

At left is the widely cultivated Queensland Silver Wattle *(Acacia podalyriifolia)*, a large shrub or small tree which grows ten or more feet high. Round, silvery phyllodes are about an inch long. A profusion of fluffy golden flowerheads are borne in late autumn and winter.

Acacia undulifolia (above) is a tall shrub from the tablelands and western slopes of New South Wales and southern Queensland. The ovate to round phyllodes are less than half an inch long, and wavy (hence specific name). Showy, pale gold flowerballs, longer than the phyllodes, are borne in summer on long, solitary stalks.

Acacia suaveolens (right) is the pale-flowered Sweet-scented Wattle common along the coast and tablelands of eastern Australia. A slender graceful shrub, it flourishes on sandstone in the poorest of soils, producing its welcome perfumed blossoms in the winter months. This acacia grows to a height of six feet, and the grey-green phyllodes, usually quite narrow, may be six or more inches long.

Australia's Golden Wattle, *Acacia pycnantha,* featured on the coat of arms and coinage, is generally accepted as the national floral emblem. Native to South Australia, Victoria and south-western New South Wales, it flourishes in hot and arid areas, holding and binding shallow sandy soil, blazoning forth in spring with a profusion of large, deep gold, scented flowerballs. It is pictured at right growing in Flinders Range, South Australia.

The Juniper Wattle, *Acacia ulicifolia* (below) carries dainty pom-poms of pale yellow in late winter and spring. Narrow phyllodes, less than an inch long, taper to a sharp point. It is one of several acacias known by the vernacular name, Prickly Moses, and is native to the eastern coast and tablelands.

Acacia linearifolia (below, right) is a tree, 15 to 30 feet high. Bark is rough and fissured; phyllodes long, narrow and pointed. Deep gold flowerballs are borne in racemes in spring.

ULICIFOLIA

ACACIA LINEARIFOLIA ▽

△ ACACIA PYCNANTHA ▽

ACACIA ELLIPTICA △

Acacia elliptica (above) is a native of tropical Queensland, Northern Territory and Western Australia. A spreading shrub, varying in height from 12 inches to six feet, and occasionally occurring as a small tree, it has silver-grey or bluish foliage. Large, bright gold flowerballs are borne in winter or early spring. The specimen pictured was photographed at Angus Downs in the Northern Territory.

Acacia ligulata (left), the Umbrella Bush or Small Cooba, has a wide range over arid inland regions. A spreading, bushy shrub, ten to 15 feet high, it has thick phyllodes and flowers in spring.

Acacia pravifolia (below) is a small rigid shrub with bright golden flowerheads and stiff, flat, triangular phyllodes, about half an inch long and tapering to a sharp point. Pods are extremely hairy. *A. pravifolia* occurs in South Australia and western New South Wales.

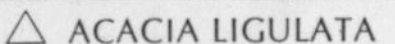

△ ACACIA LIGULATA

ACACIA PRAVIFOLIA ▽

ACACIA LONGIFOLIA ▷

A group of acacias known botanically as the Juliflorae has individual flowers massed in spikes or catkins, rather than round pom-pom balls. All the Juliflorae have leaves reduced to phyllodes. A typical member of the group is *Acacia longifolia,* pictured above, which carries its long golden fingers of blossoms in late winter and spring. This is the Sydney Golden Wattle, common in eastern Australia, especially on sandstone. Phyllodes are oblong, half an inch to an inch broad and up to seven inches long, with several prominent longitudinal veins. Pods are about six inches long, very narrow, and slightly contracted between the seeds. This wattle varies in habit from a bushy shrub to a small tree, ten to 15 feet high. A coastal variety, *A. longifolia* var. *sophorae* (sometimes listed as a separate species), has phyllodes slightly rounder, shorter, and often more leathery. It flourishes on the sandy margins of coastal lakes, sometimes maintaining an existence in the shifting dunes and salt spray of the sea shore.

ACACIA OXYCEDRUS ▽

Pictured below is *Acacia longissima,* the Narrow-leaf Wattle, an erect shrub which grows four to 12 feet high in dry sclerophyll forests of coastal Queensland, New South Wales and Victoria. Pale yellow, loose flowerheads are borne in spikes, and may be seen in any season of the year. The narrow phyllodes, four to twelve inches long, have a single prominent vein.

The spikey wattle (above) is *Acacia oyxcedrus,* a rigid, compact shrub up to ten feet high, native to temperate eastern Australia. Foliage is prickly, and attractive spikes of bright yellow flowerheads, much longer than the phyllodes, are carried in winter and spring.

The Raspberry Jam tree, *Acacia acuminata* (below) owes its

ACACIA LONGISSIMA ▽

ACACIA ACUMINATA ▽

ACACIA HAMMONDII △

△ ACACIA RESINOMARGINEA

ACACIA JULIFERA ▽

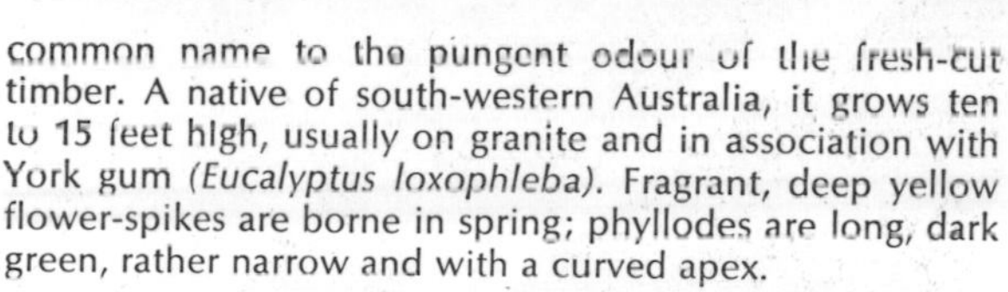

common name to the pungent odour of the fresh-cut timber. A native of south-western Australia, it grows ten to 15 feet high, usually on granite and in association with York gum *(Eucalyptus loxophleba)*. Fragrant, deep yellow flower-spikes are borne in spring; phyllodes are long, dark green, rather narrow and with a curved apex.

Acacia hammondii (above) is a spreading shrub of open habit, confined to the tropical north. Narrow, shining green phyllodes are two to three inches long, with two prominent parallel veins. Bright golden rods of flowers appear in mid-winter. It is shown here growing amid the red-rusted rocks of central Australia.

Acacia resinomarginea (above, right) is a spreading shrub or small tree which grows in sandy soil around Coolgardie and neighbouring districts in south-western Australia. Straight, narrow phyllodes are up to eight inches long and usually less than one-twelfth of an inch broad; they have a hard, hook-like apex, numerous parallel veins and crenulated margins. Short, bright gold flowering spikes are borne in pairs from May to December. The black objects in the photograph are not seed-pods, but galls.

The wattle pictured at right is *Acacia julifera*, photographed growing on remote Chasm Island in the Gulf of Carpentaria. This tall shrub or tree occurs in tropical northern Australia, extending to the north coast of New South Wales. Distinctive sickle-shaped phyllodes, up to six inches long, have prominent raised margins, and young foliage is velvety. Flower-spikes appear in spring, carried on short stalks. Pods are long and spirally twisted.

△ ACACIA ADSURGENS

ACACIA LASIOCALYX ▽

Pictured above is *Acacia adsurgens*, a wattle of the arid country in the Northern Territory and central Western Australia. An erect shrub, usually many-stemmed, it grows six to twelve feet high, and occurs in red sand, often in company with mulga and spinifex. Grey-green foliage is aromatic, and needle-like phyllodes are thick and up to six inches long. Bright golden catkins, about half an inch long, are borne in spring; pods occur in dense curly clusters.

At left is *Acacia lasiocalyx*, a diffuse shrub with very thin, sickle-shaped phyllodes, up to nine inches long and much curved at the apex. A distinctive feature of this wattle is the bluish-white colour of the branchlets and bark of the lower trunk. It occurs on granite outcrops in the Coolgardie and Avon districts of Western Australia. Bright yellow flower-spikes, about an inch long, appear from late winter to early summer.

At right is *Acacia floribunda,* the Sally Wattle, usually a large bushy shrub or small tree, though it sometimes grows to 40 feet on moist rich soil near creeks or rivers. It is fairly common on the coast and tablelands of New South Wales and eastern Victoria. Pale yellow flower-spikes are borne in spring. Phyllodes, two to five inches long and less than half an inch broad, are thin and finely veined. Pods are narrow and up to four inches long. This wattle is closely related to *Acacia longifolia,* the Sydney Golden Wattle (see page 21), and is one of several acacias commonly called Sallow or Sally wattles, a reference, not to the pale yellow flower-spikes, but to the slightly weeping, willow-like habit (willows belong to the genus *Salix*).

Acacia aneura (below) is Mulga, the predominant species of vast tracts of arid inland Australia. It is a small tree with stiff, silver-grey foliage. Phyllodes are usually very narrow (but in var. *latifolia* they are short and broad). Golden flower-spikes appear in late winter and spring; pods are flattened and winged. Mulga is well-known for its hard timber of contrasting dark brown and yellow, which takes a high polish and is much favoured for curios. Aborigines used it for their long narrow shields, or "mulgas", hence the common name. The specimen pictured is growing near Alice Springs, in the Northern Territory.

Acacia mucronata (below, right) is the Variable Sallow Wattle, pictured here growing in the Dandenongs, Victoria. Phyllodes are long, narrow, rather stiff, with three prominent veins and short hard tips. It flowers in spring.

△ ACACIA FLORIBUNDA

ACACIA MUCRONATA ▽

ACACIA ANEURA △

△ ACACIA BAILEYANA ▽

Pictured on these pages is one of Australia's most spectacular and best-known wattles, *Acacia baileyana*, the Cootamundra wattle. Native to a limited area around its name-town, Cootamundra, on the western slopes of southern New South Wales, it is now widely cultivated elsewhere in Australia and overseas.

Unlike the wattles pictured on preceding pages, Cootamundra wattle retains in maturity the feathery leaves of the seedling stage. It belongs to the Botryocephaleae, one of two exclusively-Australian groups of acacias with bipinnate foliage. Soft, silvery-grey leaves are in winter and early spring all but obscured by pendulous masses of bright golden flowerballs. A graceful, shapely, fast-growing tree, often with widespread foliage sweeping to the ground, sometimes with straight uncluttered trunk, it ranges in height from ten to 30 feet.

Cootamundra wattle has two to four pairs of pinnae (primary segments of the divided leaf) and numerous pinnules (secondary segments of the divided pinna). These tiny leaflets are a quarter of an inch long and less than one-sixteenth of an inch broad. Flowerheads are borne in panicles from the leaf axils. Straight, flat, blue-green pods are a quarter of an inch broad, and up to three inches long.

△ ACACIA DEALBATA ▽

Acacia dealbata, the Silver Wattle, of eastern Australian highlands, is pictured (above) near Jindabyne, New South Wales, with the snow-covered southern alps in the background. Bark and foliage are silvery. Usually a small to medium-sized tree, this wattle sometimes occurs as a shrub but in Tasmania attains a height of 80 or more feet. Masses of sweet-scented yellow-gold blossoms are borne in spring.

A. dealbata is shown at left beside an alpine stream at Falls Creek, Victoria, and at right on the shore of Lake Burley Griffin, Canberra.

Acacia decurrens (below) is one of several *Acacia* species known as Black Wattle; the name refers to the dark-coloured bark, which in older trees becomes rough and corrugated. A small to medium-sized tree, 12 to 40 feet high with a dense crown of dark green, feathery leaves, it occurs on the coast and tablelands of south-eastern Australia and in late winter and spring is laden with heavy, bright yellow flowerballs. *A. decurrens* has four to 12 pairs of pinnae, and widely-spaced, rather scattered pinnules, up to half an inch long. It is characterized by prominent ridges on the stems.

ACACIA DECURRENS ▽

△ ACACIA DEALBATA

△ ACACIA PARRAMATTENSIS

Acacia parramattensis (left) occurs mainly in the Sydney district, along the Hawkesbury River from Penrith to Wiseman's Ferry, and on the lower slopes and valleys of the Blue Mountains,extending to the A.C.T. Very similar to the commercially-important *Acacia mearnsii* (not illustrated) and formerly included under this species, it differs in the foliage, which in *A. mearnsii* is covered with soft, dense hairs. A shrub or small tree, six to 20 feet high, *A. parramattensis* has smooth, greenish-black trunk. Young foliage is golden-yellow, and panicles of scented flowerballs are borne throughout summer.

Acacia filicifolia (top pictures, opposite) is the Fern-leaf Wattle, a large shrub or small tree, occasionally growing to 40 feet in height. Stems and foliage are dull green to bluish-grey, clothed in soft down when young. Branchlets are less prominently angled than those of *Acacia decurrens*, pictured page 28. *A. filicifolia* has five to 14 pairs of pinnae, and numerous, crowded pinnules. It is a native of the tablelands and western slopes of New South Wales, and flowers in spring.

Acacia spectabilis (lower picture) is the Mudgee or Pilliga Wattle, common on the central western slopes of New South Wales, extending to the tablelands, western plains and southern Queensland. A shrub or small tree, ten to 15 feet high, slender and often pendulous, it has powdery white bark and silvery foliage. Large, bright golden flowerballs are carried on long sprays in late winter and spring.

Acacia pubescens, the Downy Wattle (below, right) grows three to ten feet high. Stems and young foliage are clothed in long, soft, silvery hairs. This wattle, now rare in nature, is a popular garden subject, cultivated overseas in glasshouses. Bright yellow scented blossoms are borne in spring.

Acacia trachyphloia (lower picture, far right) is a recently-described species with a limited distribution on the south coast and tablelands of New South Wales (from Termeil southward to Broulee beach) usually along creek flats in heavy alluvial soil but also on mountainsides in dry sclerophyll forests. Branchlets are pendulous, young tips a very bright gold, soft and velvety. It flowers in spring.

ACACIA SPECTABILIS ▽

△ ACACIA FILICIFOLIA ▽

ACACIA PUBESCENS ▽

ACACIA TRACHYPHLOIA ▽

ACACIA ELATA ▽

ACACIA BOTRYCEPHALA ▽

The Cedar Wattle, *Acacia elata* (above) is one of the tallest of acacias, often reaching a height of 90 feet. It occurs in moist, sheltered gullies and on the margins of rainforests in the Blue Mountains, southern tablelands, and Hawkesbury River district of New South Wales. The common name refers to a supposed likeness to the Cedar of Lebanon; it has also been called Pepper Tree Wattle because its foliage resembles that of the Pepper Tree *(Schinus molle)*. It is an excellent shade tree, fast-growing and longer-lived than most acacias. Dark green, shiny, compound leaves, 12 to 18 inches long with individual leaflets up to two inches long and half an inch broad, are massed in a thick crown. Clusters of large, creamy, globular flower-heads are borne in late summer and autumn.

Left: *Acacia botrycephala* (syn. *A. discolor*), the Sunshine Wattle, flowers for nine months of the year, from early autumn to late spring, bearing its large sprays of loose, pale cream to deep yellow flowerballs most profusely in mid-winter. A native of coastal eastern Australia, this wattle usually occurs as a shrub, four or five feet high. Pinnules (eight to 16 pairs) are paler on the undersurface; there are one to six pairs of pinnae.

The second group of exclusively-Australian bipinnate wattles is the Pulchellae, typified by *Acacia pulchella*, shown at right blooming with red and green Kangaroo Paw in King's Park, near Perth. A small shrub, rarely more than three feet high, with compound leaves and sharp spines at the leaf-stalks, it flowers from May to October and is confined to the south-western province of Western Australia.

ACACIA PULCHELLA ▽

◁ ACACIA PENTADENIA

ACACIA DRUMMONDII ▽

Acacia pentadenia (above) is the Karri Wattle. A shrub six to ten feet high, it grows in association with Karri gums in the extreme south-western corner of Australia. The flowering season is from July to December.

Above, right, is *Acacia drummondii,* also a native of the south-west, a compact small shrub, 18 inches to three feet high, with fine, light green, fern-like foliage. Spectacular, vivid yellow flower-spikes are borne profusely from midwinter to spring.

Acacia farnesiana, below, belongs to the Gummiferae group of bipinnate wattles, of which only a handful of species occur in the tropical regions of this country. This wattle is the only indigenous *Acacia* species which Australia shares with other parts of the world; it occurs naturally in all five continents and is extensively cultivated in southern France for perfumery oil. Some believe that it was introduced into Australia by the Aborigines, before the coming of the white man. Large, sweetly-scented, deep yellow flowerballs are borne in spring.

ACACIA FARNESIANA ▷

RIVER RED GUM (*Eucalyptus camaldulensis*), growing on the banks of the Edwards River, near Deniliquin, New South Wales. The common name refers to the colour of the timber, which is hard, durable and often figured. The tree itself is usually whitish, with persistent bark, and is known as the White Gum in some districts. This splendid and picturesque gumtree follows the watercourses throughout inland Australia, thriving in areas subject to periodic flooding and withstanding great extremes of temperature. It grows to 60 or more feet high and has a wide graceful crown and short-barrelled, heavy bole, usually covered at the butt with rough, reddish-brown bark. The narrow, pendulous, sickle-shaped leaves are up to nine inches long and an inch wide. In summer the River Red Gum is covered with a profusion of small creamy flowers, and it is a valuable honey producer. The little round buds taper to a point.

The range of the River Red Gum is shown by these specimens. Above it is seen growing on lush pastures by the banks of the Murrumbidgee, near Wagga Wagga, New South Wales. Left, it grows beside the Finke River in the Ormiston Gorge, central Australia.

This tree is perhaps the most widely distributed of all the eucalypts, and extends right across the continent, from just over the Great Dividing Range in the east, almost to the coast of Western Australia. It is the gumtree made famous by the paintings of Hans Heysen, and is widely cultivated overseas. Yet because it does not extend into the narrow coastal strip, many Australians have never seen it growing in its natural state.

The trunks of the River Red Gum, often twisted and contorted by nature into weird and decorative shapes, are tall and shaft-like when grown under good conditions. The bark is often attractively streaked and mottled with red, grey and white. In the example above, five huge trunks spring from a single root system. This particular tree is growing in the dry bed of the Todd River, near Alice Springs, central Australia. At left, a well grown specimen illustrates the colourful bark of this species. The River Red Gum is a rapid grower, and a seedling will grow twenty or more feet in three or four years, even under adverse conditions.

It is an excellent shade and shelter tree, and its deep roots permit grass to grow right up to the trunk. The role of the River Red Gum in the ecology of inland Australia is remarkable. Everywhere it can be seen, holding the soil, safeguarding the river banks, preventing and alleviating flooding.

MOUNTAIN ASH (*Eucalyptus regnans*). Noblest of Australian trees, and recognised as the tallest hardwood in the world, the mighty Mountain Ashes are found only in eastern Victoria and Tasmania. In the latter state they are sometimes called Swamp Gums, and other common names are Giant Gum, Tasmanian Oak, White Mountain Ash, and Stringy-barked Gum.

The last-mentioned name refers to the bark, rough and dark at the base and smooth white above and on the upper limbs. The trunk is straight and smooth, and may tower for 200 or more feet to the first branches.

There have been many tales told of Mountain Ashes reaching a height of 400 and more feet, but these measurements have never been verified, although several over 300 feet high have been authenticated.

ALPINE ASH (*Eucalyptus delegatensis*), also called the Red Mountain Ash, is not quite so tall as *E. regnans*, pictured opposite, but is still a giant, growing to 200 and more feet in the southern tablelands of New South Wales, Victoria and Tasmania. The ones pictured are growing by the Alpine Way, near Mount Kosciusko. Bark is rough and fibrous on the lower half or third of the trunk, and a smooth creamy white above. Mature leaves are large, up to nine inches long and two inches wide, and a shining green; juvenile leaves are broader and shorter, and a smoky blue in colour.

SPOTTED GUM (*Eucalyptus maculata*). This lovely, tall-growing tree with dappled trunk and shining crown of large dark green leaves, is a native of the shale country along coastal New South Wales and southern Queensland.

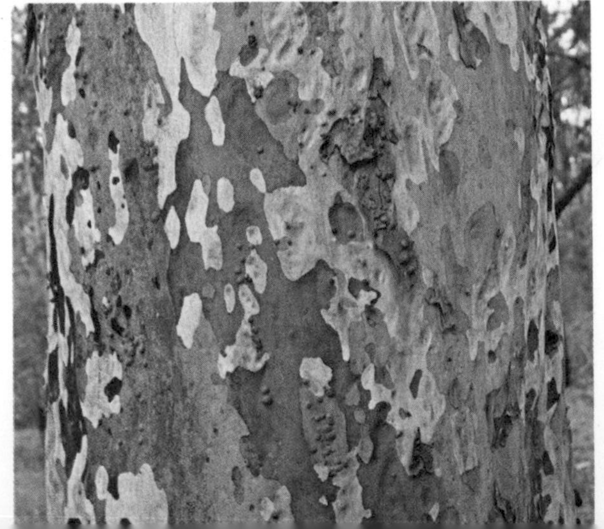

The Spotted Gum grows to a hundred or more feet high, though many specimens would be smaller than this. It is very hardy, and a rapid grower. Though it does not occur naturally in the sandstone areas around Sydney, it has proved itself adaptable to gardens there, and a fine stand of young trees can be seen at the Forestry Commission's nursery at West Pennant Hills. The bark is shed in circular flakes, producing the mottled appearance. Creamy white flowers are carried in autumn and winter, though, in common with many eucalypts, they do not appear every year. As an ornamental, this tree has proved itself adaptable to a wide range of soils, and it is moderately drought-resistant, though requiring protection from frost in the early stages. It is a valued winter-flowering honey tree, and the timber has many commercial uses. Unlike most other Australian trees, it often occurs in almost pure stands, and the massed effect of the smooth, clean trunks is most attractive.

YELLOW BOX (*Eucalyptus melliodora*). This shapely tree with wide spreading habit and drooping, bluish-grey foliage is a honey source of first importance, regarded by many as the finest in the world. It is also prized as an ornamental and valuable shade tree, and the pale yellow, close-textured timber is very durable. It is drought resistant and frost resistant—indeed, an all-purpose tree! The Australian Boxes are a group of eucalypts with fine scaly or flaky. bark. This one has a characteristic inner bark, described by noted botanist J. H. Maiden as "yellow as the proverbial guinea". From this comes the common name; the specific name, *melliodora*, is from *mellis*, honey, and *odora*, sweetly scented, and refers to the heavy perfume of the honey-laden blossoms. The little fruits are round and have a characteristic narrow rim. Yellow Box is found on the tablelands and western slopes from Queensland to Victoria. The trees pictured were photographed in morning mist and frost near Goulburn, New South Wales.

MANNA or RIBBON GUM (*Eucalyptus viminalis*). The deciduous bark of this white gum is shed in long ribbons, giving the tree its quaint, characteristic appearance and its common name, Ribbon Gum. The other vernacular name, Manna Gum, refers to the white sugary substance which is excreted on the leaves. Widely distributed on the tablelands of New South Wales, Victoria, South Australia and Tasmania, it attains a height of 60 or more feet in the moist mountain gullies.

The SNOW GUM (*Eucalyptus pauciflora*), or White Sally, as it is sometimes called, is widely distributed in the tableland districts of New South Wales, Victoria and Tasmania. Varying from shrub-like growth to a handsome tree of moderate size, this hardy gum is conspicuous in the Snowy Mountains region. The pale bark is often prettily streaked. It has great powers of endurance, as demonstrated by the specimen pictured above, which survives near Jindabyne, New South Wales, though blown over and almost uprooted. The twin trees, top left, are growing near Deloraine, Tasmania.

ALPINE SNOW GUM (*Eucalyptus niphophila*). Twisted and pummelled by the constant fierce winds, this species grows only at high elevations, and marks the limit of tree growth on the Australian Alps. The weatherbeaten trunks are often twisted into strange and beautiful shapes, and the pale bark, streaked with vivid reds, pinks, greens and yellow, gleams against the snow. Because of the bleak, harsh environment, it often assumes a shrubby, mallee form of growth, with several stems springing from a protected, bulbous rootstock. Closely related to *E. pauciflora*, pictured opposite, it can be distinguished by slight differences in the buds and fruit, which in the Alpine Snow Gum are ashy-grey in colour. Photographs on this page were taken on the slopes of Mount Kosciusko, at Thredbo Valley and Charlotte Pass.

NORTHERN SCRIBBLY GUM (*Eucalyptus signata*), growing in the Glass House Mountains area, southern Queensland. The pale trunks of these trees are colourfully blotched with grey and rusty red, and marked with characteristic, insect-caused scribbles. On the opposite page is the best known of the scribblies, the BROAD-LEAFED SCRIBBLY GUM (*E. haemastoma*). For long the Cinderella of the Sydney district, it is now recognised as one of the loveliest of Australian trees, and something to be treasured. This tree flourishes in the poor soil of the Hawkesbury sandstone area, where it graces the steep rocky slopes, sometimes growing into a shapely, spreading tree, sometimes forming mallee-like thickets.

Whatever its habit of growth, it always seems to assume a graceful, free flowing shape. The multi-coloured trunk often has a satiny sheen, and the contrasting creamy white and slate blue bark is marked with the spectacular red scribbles. The large, tough leaves are silvery-blue in the sunlight. Flowers are creamy-white.

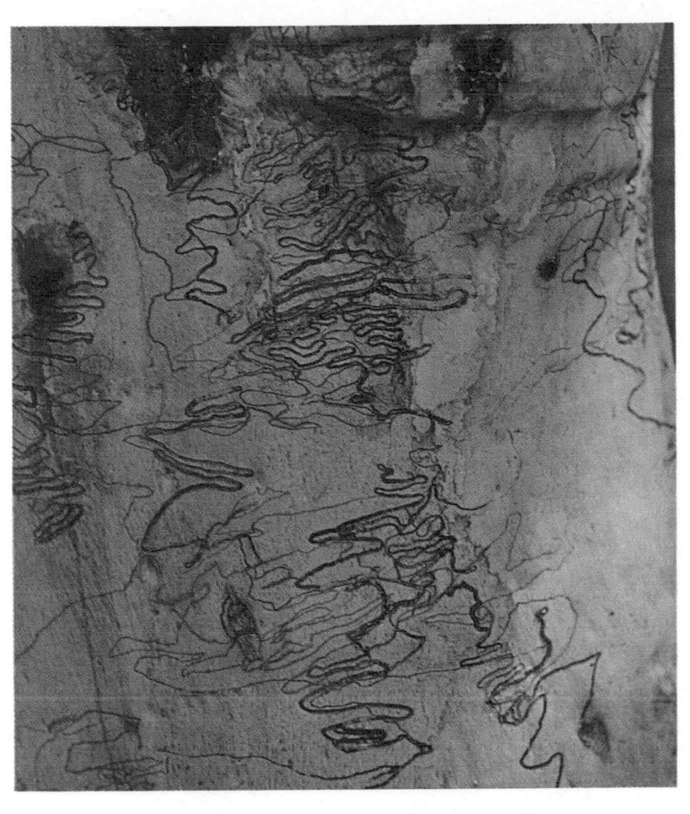

MUGGA IRONBARK (*Eucalyptus sideroxylon*), pictured above, has dark, deeply furrowed bark and dense, silvery blue foliage. It is a slender, upright tree which can grow 50 to 100 feet, but is usually much smaller. The large flowers vary from white to red, and a variety often grown in gardens, has consistently pink flowers. The Mugga Ironbark is quick growing, drought and frost resistant, and does well in poor soils. Above left is the SILVER-LEAFED IRONBARK or BLUE MOP, (*E. melanophloia*), a small tree, often crooked in growth. The broad leaves of this very hardy tree have a silvery sheen. A native of inland New South Wales and Queensland, it does well on most soils and withstands extremes of heat and cold.

The Ironbark group can be distinguished by their rough, deeply furrowed bark, persistent on the trunks and lower branches. They are among the best honey producers in the world, both in quality and quantity, and include many valuable timber trees.

The NORTHERN GREY IRONBARK (*Eucalyptus siderophloia*) is shown above growing on dairy pasture near Maitland, New South Wales, in company with the Forest Red Gum (*E. tereticornis*). It occurs as a large forest tree on the coast and western slopes of New South Wales and Queensland, and is very adaptable, doing well in poor sandy soils, and reaching as high as 100 feet under more favourable conditions. At right are the flowers and fruit of *E. paniculata*, the Grey Ironbark. A close-up of the bark is shown on the opposite page.

A page of tree curiosities, some demonstrating the eucalypt's amazing powers of survival. At right a River Red Gum, though blown over and its roots torn from the ground, has re-established itself from its branches, and a coppice of slender trees replaces the fallen giant. Below, another River Red Gum; winds have bent it, bushfires have burnt it hollow; lightning has lopped its branches, and they have grown together, forming a huge circle. Below right, a Bloodwood, *E. terminalis*, blends its brick-red, flaky bark into the spectacular background of Australia's Ayers Rock, the largest monolith in the world. Top right, a eucalypt at Adventure Bay, Bruny Island, Tasmania. Beautiful even in death, this tree is part of Australia's history; it was flourishing when Captain Cook and other early explorers landed in the quiet bay. Below this, a Flowered Box (*E. largiflorens*) from which aborigines have cut bark for a canoe. Other pictures show the eucalypts' capacity to develop protective rubbing pads where branches from two trees are thrust together.

BLAKELY'S RED GUM (*Eucalyptus blakelyi*). This handsome ornamental tree is also valued for its timber and honey. It is common on the western slopes of New South Wales and Queensland, occurring naturally on damp, alluvial soils and therefore a very suitable choice for planting in low-lying or swampy ground. The smooth bark is often beautifully mottled, and the thick leaves are pendulous. It flowers profusely throughout spring and summer, and like most eucalypts, propagates readily from seed. The generic name Eucalyptus means "well-covered", and refers to the characteristic fusing of the petals into a bud cap (operculum) which completely covers the developing blossom until thrust off by the expanding stamems. This is the distinguishing feature by which eucalypts can be identified. The closely-related Angophoras produce similar blossoms of crowded stamens, and a gumnut-like fruit, but they do not have the characteristic cap of the flowerbud from which the eucalypt derives its name.

NEW ENGLAND PEPPERMINT (*Eucalyptus nova-anglica*). This tree occurs naturally on the tablelands of New South Wales and Queensland, but will also grow very well under cultivation in coastal districts. The leaves are bluish-green, and the buds ash-coloured. Sometimes called Blue Tip, it often retains its juvenile foliage, and it is very decorative when the silvery blue young leaves contrast with the darker, blue-green crown. It flowers in summer and autumn, producing small, dense clusters of blossoms. The Peppermint below is a form of *Eucalyptus amygdalina* and has yellowish-green foliage. This tree was photographed near Mount King William, Tasmania, and the species is confined to that state. Peppermints are a group of eucalypts whose foliage has a strong aromatic odour; in some cases they are valuable commercial sources of essential oils. Many are graceful in habit, with weeping foliage. Barks are greyish, short-fibred and interlaced, persistent over the trunks and larger branches.

THIN-LEAFED STRINGYBARK (*Eucalyptus eugenioides*) growing in company with a gum near Springbrook, Queensland. Notice the rubbing pad between the twin trunks of the gum — without the ability to develop this protection, the tree would eventually ringbark itself, and die. *E. eugenioides* is a tall, graceful tree, growing to 100 feet high, and it flowers in summer and autumn. The Stringybarks are a group of eucalypts with rough, close, fibrous bark covering both trunk and branches. Unlike that of the Ironbarks, it pulls away in wide, stringy strips. In some species this bark is so thick and durable that it was used in slabs for building rough dwellings and shelters — the traditional bark humpy or slab hut. Bark colour is either grey or reddish brown, and most members of the group are to be found on the eastern coast and tablelands, from southern Queensland to Tasmania.

The Stringybarks are usually tall, well-balanccd, stately trees, Below, left, is the MESSMATE STRINGYBARK (*Eucalyptus obliqua*), not a typical stringybark because, although the bark is rough and fibrous to the ends of the branches, the fibres are not so long and stringy as in other members of the group. This tree is called "Messmate" because it frequently grows in association (messmating) with other, more typical stringybarks. At lower right is a close-up of the trunk. This particular tree is dying, and the bark is falling away, disclosing its rough, fibrous composition. The other two photographs are of typical stringybarks, both growing on the south coast of New South Wales. Stringybarks include many commercial timber trees.

FOREST RED GUM (*Eucalyptus tereticornis*). One of the finest of our forest trees, this tall gum is widely distributed on the coastal districts and ranges of eastern Australia, and is one of the few eucalypts to extend across the Torres Strait to Papua. It is very adaptable, and flourishes on a wide variety of soils. The trunk, in parts smooth and in parts retaining strips of older bark, is mottled slaty-blue and grey, and an alternative common name is Slaty Gum. This tree grows to a hundred or more feet, and the deep red timber is very durable. It flowers prolifically from mid-winter to summer, and is valued as a honey tree. It can be recognised by its horn-shaped buds.

GHOST GUM (*Eucalyptus papuana*), is the typical eucalypt of the dry interior. The stark white moulded trunk and boughs are ghostly in the moonlight, hence the common name. This tree maintains a perpetual battle for existence, thrusting through the barren red rocks and existing in seemingly impossible situations. Always graceful, even in adversity, it assumes truly noble proportions when conditions are more favourable, as shown by the trees pictured on this page. The one above was photographed at Trephina Gorge, central Australia, and that at right near Alice Springs.

This is the tree which aboriginal artist Albert Namatjira loved to paint, against its natural background of brilliant blue sky and harsh red rock. A short-trunked tree with spreading branches, it is essentially a tropical gum, found in arid areas of Queensland, Northern Territory, Western Australia and Papua. It grows to about 30 feet, and should be easy to establish in dry, hot regions.

The amazing adaptability of the eucalypt is shown on these and the next pages. Above, a graceful Ghost Gum thrusts its gleaming white trunk from the red rock face of Trephina Gorge, central Australia. Top right, River Red Gums hold the soil on the banks of the Murrumbidgee, New South Wales, flourishing even though their roots are perpetually waterlogged. Lower right, the mallee form of growth adopted by many eucalypts when faced with harsh conditions of soil or rainfall. Instead of one main shaft, they develop numerous slender stems from an underground rootstock, which is protected from fires and extremes of heat and cold, and also acts as a storehouse of food

and nourishment during dry periods. Most eucalypts when subjected to harsh conditions have the potential to maintain themselves as mallees, and the reverse is also true — many true mallees when grown under good conditions are capable of developing as a single trunk. Top right, a gnarled and twisted eucalypt grows from bare rock at King's Canyon, central Australia. Lower right, the ubiquitous Ghost Gum of central Australia fights an incredible battle for survival amongst the rocks of Palm Valley, Northern Territory.

Extremes of heat and cold have wrought the eucalypts pictured above into flowing shapes that delight the eye. The Ghost Gum at left, growing on ironstone hills near Wittenoom Gorge, Western Australia, has been bent by the prevailing winds, and the red dust of the inland is deeply embedded in its white trunk. The Alpine Snow Gum above is growing in the Perisher Valley, near Mount Kosciusko, Australia's highest mountain. Icy winds and weight of snow have moulded its trunk into a sweeping curve, and its roots grip wide and deep into the bank to support the cantilevered weight of the horizontal trunk.

At left, eucalypts grow almost in the sea at Bruny Island, Tasmania, and River Red Gums stand in floodwater near Balranald, New South Wales.

There are over 400 eucalypts, and one species or another can be found in all but the treeless desert areas. They thrive in both tropical and temperate regions, occupying exposed positions and sheltered valleys, growing in rich soil or the most infertile sand and rock. They are found in dry and wet sites, even swamps in places, and range from stunted desert and alpine species to the majestic Mountain Ash.

MORETON BAY ASH (*Eucalyptus tesselaris*). Despite its common name, this tall graceful tree belongs to the bloodwood group of eucalypts. A smooth gleaming white on the upper trunk and branches, it has persistent, tesselated bark at the butt. The leaves are narrow and pointed, and it blooms in summer. This tree is fairly widely distributed in hot dry areas of Australia, occurring in Queensland, northern New South Wales, central and western Australia. It usually favours fertile soils, and is regarded as a sign of good grazing country. Above right is a GREY GUM, *Eucalyptus major*. The dark grey bark of this tree is rough and flaky on the lower trunk, peeling off to reveal a glowing orange higher up the tree. It occurs in northern New South Wales and Queensland, and demonstrates the dramatic colour effects caused by the eucalypt's deciduous bark.

MARRI (*Eucalyptus calophylla*), right, is a west Australian species widely cultivated for its large, showy, pink or white flowers, which are carried well above the foliage. It is a close relative of the well-known scarlet-flowered *Eucalyptus ficifolia*, but is a sturdier tree. Often straggly in nature, under cultivation it will grow into a well-shaped, straight tree.

COOLABAH (*Eucalyptus microtheca*) is shown at right growing in the Ord River area. This tree flourishes beside inland watercourses and billabongs, and when found away from surface water, its presence is a sign of underground moisture, not far below the ground. The tragedies and triumphs of the inland are personified in the Coolabah. Its shade has succoured many a weary traveller, and sheltered the bones of others less fortunate. It was a Coolabah tree on which Brahe carved the words "Dig" — a message to ill-fated explorers Burke and Wills that supplies of food were buried beneath its boughs. The jolly swagman of the popular Australian song, "Waltzing Matilda", camped in the shade of the Coolabah. The Coolabah belongs to the box group, and an alternative common name is Flooded Box.

MOUNTAIN GUM (*Eucalyptus dalrympleana*), below is a fairly large tree of the highlands of New South Wales and Victoria. It can reach 150 feet in good deep soils.

Top left, opposite page: A BLOODWOOD, *Eucalyptus dichromophloia*, grows in the brilliant dry sunshine of north west Australia. A prolific honey-producer, this tree is weighed down with blossoms so copiously filled with nectar that the honey drips on the ground. Bloodwoods are so called because they exude a reddish kino that stains the wood deep red. Most are ornamental, and they include important honey trees.

Top right, opposite page: A famous KARRI (*Eucalyptus diversicolor*), growing near Gloucester, Western Australia. The cabin at the top is a fire lookout, and the tree is 220 feet tall. This species is confined to the south western corner of Australia, and the heavy, reddish-brown timber is valuable.

Lower left, opposite page, is a TIMOR GUM (*Eucalyptus alba*), one of the few deciduous eucalypts. It withstands waterlogged conditions during monsoonal rains, and its range extends through the islands north of Australia, to Timor.

Lower right, opposite page, is the POPLAR GUM (*Eucalyptus bigalerita*).

Below: Blossom of *E. torquata*, the Coral Gum. Top right: *E. leucoxylon*. Centre: Colourful young leaves of a Stringy-bark. Below right: Blossom of *E. porosa*, a Mallee.

The blossom at left is that of the Western Australian Scarlet-flowered Gum, *Eucalyptus ficifolia*. It is perhaps the best known of the flowering gumtrees. Below is an equally spectacular but lesser-known blossom, that of *Eucalyptus miniata*, the tropical Woollybutt. This small tree is found in warmer parts of Australia.

▲ *B. serratifolia* releases seeds after bushfire; note also new growth

Australia's banksias bear the name of Joseph Banks, the botanist and "father of Australia", who accompanied Captain James Cook on his voyage of discovery in 1770. He it was who collected the first specimens on the shores of the bay Cook later named Botany because of "the great quantity of New Plants Mr Banks and Dr Solander collected in this place", and the genus *Banksia* was subsequently named in his honour by the younger Linné.
There are over 50 species of *Banksia*. With the exception of the tropical *B. dentata,* which extends to New Guinea, they are found only in Australia, occurring in all States but most abundantly in the west, where there are about 40 endemic species. They belong to the Proteaceae, a large family almost wholly confined to the southern hemisphere, with its greatest development in Australia. This family

▼ *B. serratifolia* blooming on Frazer Island, Qld., in August

◀ *B. serratifolia* at Port Stephens, N.S.W., in March

includes the spectacular waratah and the spider-flowered grevilleas; the name is derived from Proteus, the Greek god of the sea who could assume many forms, an allusion to the remarkable diversity found among members, even within the same genus. Banksias, for example, range from prostrate shrubs of the sand plains, with stems creeping underground and only leaves and flowerheads visible, to trees 50 or more feet high, with massive furrowed butts and gnarled branches. Leaves vary from the fine, heath-like foliage of *B. ericifolia* to the foot-long, leathery leaves of *B. robur*. Slender, stalkless flowers are usually borne in crowded, spiralling rows around the thick woody axis of a terminal spike (an exception is the holly-leafed *B. ilicifolia* which carries flowers in dense heads) but they vary in size and colour from the squat, scarlet and gold flowerheads of the Waratah Banksia *(B. coccinea)* to the slender, foot-long spikes of glowing orange which blaze like torches from the fine-leafed foliage of *B. ericifolia,* and the massive, brilliant green inflorescence of *B. robur,* sombrely black-tipped and framed by a circle of huge, olive-green, shining leaves.

As with some wattles (mulga and brigalow) and some eucalypts (the mallee) banksias have given their name to those areas of country where they form the dominant growth. Southern Queensland's sandy coastal strip of lakes and dunes is called the wallum, an Aboriginal word once used by local tribes to describe *Banksia serratifolia* (syn. *B. aemula)* a small spreading tree or large shrub which binds the hind dunes of Australia's eastern coast in scattered localities from the Sydney district of New South Wales to the threshold of the tropics, growing in profusion on Fraser Island, that massive sand dune, 70-odd miles long, which was isolated from the coast of Queensland by the rising seas of the last ice age and now lies, luxuriant with rainforests and jewelled with deep, freshwater lakes, a pendulous guardian of the Great Barrier Reef.

▲Hairpin banksia, *B. spinulosa,* Blue Mountains, N.S.W., in April

▼*B. spinulosa* growing at Kanangra Walls, N.S.W.

▼*B. spinulosa* in bud

▼ Hairpin banksia, Lake Macquarie, near Newcastle, N.S.W.

▲ Mountain gullies near Kanangra Walls. *B. spinulosa* grows on the slopes and *B. ericifolia* on the tops

The wallum banksia closely resembles that other eastern banksia of the sandy coastal heathlands *B. serrata* (pictured and described pages 16 to 19) specimens of which were collected by Banks himself at Botany Bay in 1770. Botanists differentiate mainly by the stigma of the flower (egg-shaped in *B. serratifolia* and cylindrical in *B. serrata)* but the layman—bushwalker or gardener—is guided more by habit of growth and colour of flowerhead. *B. serratifolia* rarely grows more than 10, or at the most, 15 feet high; it is a spreading tree or shrub, branching from the base. Flower spikes are golden or yellowish-green. *B. serrata* forms quite a large tree which can grow to 30 or more feet high, with a massive, gnarled main trunk; flower spikes are silvery green and velvety in bud. Leaves of both species are evenly serrated.

The hairpin banksia *(B. spinulosa)* is an eastern species which extends from Victoria through New South Wales to Queensland, growing in isolated areas on the coast and occurring in a slightly different form on the Blue Mountains of New South Wales. It is an attractive bushy shrub or small tree, usually straggling in habit and rarely developing a definite trunk. The handsome flower spikes, 6 or 8 inches long, are orange-bronze in colour, studded with purple-

▼*B. spinulosa*

▲ Silver banksia, *B. marginata*, Cape Barren Island, Bass Strait, in March

black "hairpins" of wiry hooked styles. Crowded leaves are up to 3 inches long, very narrow, three-toothed at the tip and occasionally finely serrated along the margins, which, in the typical form, are tightly rolled back to the mid-rib (leaf margin characteristics vary somewhat on the form which grows on the slopes of Kanangra Walls

B. spinulosa is closely allied to *B. collina*, the hill banksia or "golden candlestick", which has a similar range and occurs as a shrub or very small tree on the hillsides of the east coast and tablelands. Flower-spikes of the hill banksia vary in colour from honey-gold to purple-bronze; they are adorned with hooked, shining black pins similar to those of *B. spinulosa*. The two species are distinguished mainly by the leaves, which, in *B. collina*, always have a white undersurface and are usually coarsely and evenly serrated along the recurved margins; though fairly narrow (¼") they are noticeably wider than those of *B. spinulosa*.

Another eastern species, the silver banksia, *B. marginata*, ranges from South Australia and Tasmania northward almost to the Queensland border. The popular name refers to the silvery undersurface of the small narrow leaves and an alternative common name is tree honeysuckle — like most banksias it is a valued source of nectar and pollen.

▼ *B. marginata*, Kanangra Walls, April

▲ *B. marginata* in bud, Flinders Island, Bass Strait

Lichens grow on *B. marginata* in the moist high valleys of the Australian Alps ▶

▲Velvety bracts of *B. marginata*, after flowers have fa

▲ *B. marginata* (Flinders Island, Bass Strait)

Silver banksia is a dense bushy shrub or small tree, sometimes growing to 30 or more feet high but always spreading in habit. Flowers, soft lemon yellow in colour, are borne profusely from spring to early winter; they remain for some time on the spike, persisting after death as an orange-brown fuzz, eventually turning grey before being shed to reveal the rhachis (floral axis) clothed in soft, velvety, rich red plush. The tree is usually crowded with spikes at different stages of development — pale, slender and candle-like in bud, fluffy gold in full bloom, sheathed in velvet when the withered, barren flowers have fallen.

Flower-spikes are smaller than those of the two species previously discussed, rarely being more than 3 inches long; styles, unlike the "hairpins" of *B. spinulosa* and *B. collina,* are finally straight or only gently curved upwards from near the base. Leaves are rarely more than 2 inches long, blunt-tipped, with a prominent notch at the apex. They may be either entire or coarsely serrated, silvery on the undersurface and tawny-tipped when young. New foliage is covered with long soft hairs.

This banksia has a varied habitat; it grows on the 90-mile Desert of South Australia and the sea-lashed islands of Bass Strait, on the heathlands and gorges of the Hawkesbury sandstone country and on the high slopes of the Australian Alps, in Kosciusko National Park and along the Alpine Way.

The coast banksia or white honeysuckle, *B. integrifolia,* is the old man of the sea which colonizes the cliffs and dunes of the eastern coast from the Port Phillip district in Victoria to southern Queensland, often forming groves right at the water's edge, withstanding sea blast and shifting sand, leaning gnarled, grotesque branches out over the ocean. It is, however, a versatile tree, equally at home in the high country and not uncommon on the Blue Mountains of New South Wales and the Grampians in Victoria. It can be seen growing at altitudes of above 5000 feet on Point Lookout near Ebor on the New England tablelands, and extends inland down the western slopes of the Great Dividing Range.

One of the largest of the eastern banksias, it can attain a height of 50 feet or more, though also occasionally occurring as a stunted shrub. It flowers all year round, bearing masses of honey-laden, pale yellow flower-spikes 6 or more inches long, which attract birds, bees and honey-eating marsupials.

▼ *B. integrifolia,* Lion Island, N.S.W

▲ Coast banksia or white honeysuckle, *B. integrifolia,* at Ulladulla, N.S.W.

▲ Leaves and bud of *B. integrifolia*. Yellowing indicates only that a leaf is old, and about to fall

▲*B. integrifolia,* blooming in July on Frazer Island, Qld.

▲ Cob of *B. integrifolia,* Lovett's Bay, N.S.W.

Leaves are dark glossy green, silver-lined with matted, felt-like hair. They are up to 5 inches long, half an inch or more broad, and sometimes wedge-shaped at the apex, with prominent veins on the undersurface. The specific botanical name, *integrifolia,* refers to the leaf-margins, which are mostly smooth and unbroken (entire), though this is not an infallible guide as edges are sometimes irregularly toothed, particularly in juvenile foliage.

Floral parts of *Banksia* are in fours; the perianth (petals and sepals) is tubular and slender, with sepals petal-like in appearance so that it seems each individual flower has four petals, silken-haired and very narrow. The four stamens are opposite the flower-segments and fused to them; only the anthers are free, seated in a spoon-shaped lobe at the top. The style is prominent, long and wiry; it protrudes from a slit in the floral tube to form a characteristic loop while the stigma is still held captive. When the stigma is set free, the style is either finally straight or permanently hooked, and this is a characteristic by which the various species of *Banksia* can be roughly differentiated.

Flowers of *Banksia* are stalkless, borne in dense terminal spikes or heads containing a thousand or more individual blooms crowded in spiralling rows around a thick woody axis. These floral spikes develop into woody fruiting cones, on which the colourful, withered, barren flowers often persist for some time as a dry, bristly fuzz, with isolated woody seed-capsules protruding at scattered intervals (in the majority of *Banksia* species, curiously few flowers develop to maturity). The woody capsules (follicles) eventually split into two, revealing a pair of paper-thin winged seeds; in most species they remain closed until the cone is broken off or is seared by the heat of passing bushfires. *B. integrifolia,* pictured above, is an exception. It spits its seeds out when ripe, releasing them without warning.

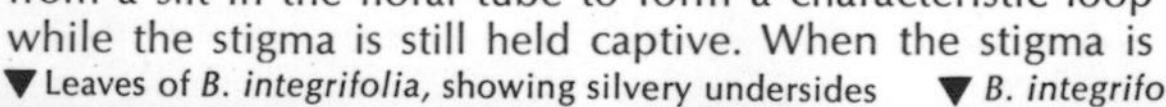

▼Leaves of *B. integrifolia,* showing silvery undersides

▼ *B. integrifolia,* Frazer Island, Qld.

▼ *B. integrifolia* on the sandy sea-shore, Mollymook, N.S.W.

▲Flowers of the heath-leafed banksia, *B. ericifolia,* open from the top of the spike first

▲Actual specimens of *B. ericifolia* collected by Banks and Solander

◀Distinctive leaves and fruiting cob of *B. ericifolia*

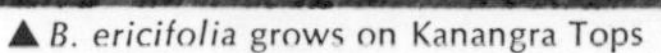

▲ *B. ericifolia* grows on Kanangra Tops

▲ *B. ericifolia* blooming at West Head, Ku-ring-gai Chase, in February

The heath-leafed banksia, *B. ericifolia,* is the largest-flowered and most colourful of the eastern species. Slender spikes are brilliant fiery orange and may be up to 12 or 14 inches long. A shapely large shrub or densely crowned small tree, it is a native of the sandy coastal areas of New South Wales, common on the Hawkesbury sandstone around Sydney and extending to the Blue Mountains. Foliage is distinctive and most attractive; tiny, rigid, dark green leaves are carried in crowded whorls around slender branches, with new growth at the tips light in colour so that the plant appears multi-hued even when not in bloom. Main trunk and larger branches are relatively smooth, mottled with bronze and various shades of grey. *B. ericifolia* blooms from autumn to early spring, carrying vivid torches throughout the cooler months, and all year long the fruiting cones, studded with scattered seed capsules, peer from the fine heath-like foliage, full, velvety lips tightly pursed. Flowers, unlike those of most banksias, usually open at the top of the spike first, and the style remains permanently hooked, even in death. The half-inch long leaves are very narrow, notched at the apex; margins are tightly rolled back. This banksia is said to be the first Australian native plant collected by Sir Joseph Banks, at Botany Bay in 1770.

▲ Smooth bark of *B. ericifolia* (Galston Gorge, N.S.W.)

◀ Tiny honey-eating pigmy possum feeds on *B. ericifolia*

In marked contrast is the massive-leafed swamp banksia, *B. robur,* which grows as a low bushy shrub rarely more than 5 or 6 feet high, in open swampy country on the sandy lowlands of coastal New South Wales and Queensland. Vivid green flowers, brushed with black, are carried in dense squat spikes, 6 or 8 inches long, 3 or 4 inches in diameter, framed by a circle of young branches and stiff, irregularly toothed leaves, a foot or more long and up to 3 inches wide, dark shining green with bright yellow, prominent mid-rib. Branches and the undersurface of mature leaves are covered with the rusty brown velvet of closely matted short hairs, and, as with all banksias, the slender stalkless flowers are surrounded by velvety-brown bracts. The style is spreading, and the stigma very small. This is one of the *Banksia* species where the style is finally straight, though it splits the floral tube to form the characteristic loop while the stigma is still held captive. The huge leaves are bluntly egg-shaped, tending to be broader at the end, and are strongly reticulate underneath.

Pictured opposite is *B. aspleniifolia,* which occurs on poor sandy soils and rocky ridges along the east coast, growing particularly abundantly on the Hawkesbury sandstones around Sydney. For too long this delightful little banksia has been regarded as a "poor cousin" of the more striking eastern species, to be grubbed out indiscriminately as more

▲ Swamp banksia, *B. robur,* Ku-ring-gai Chase, February ▼

▼ Leaves of *B. aspleniifolia* (Galston Gorge, N.S.W.)

▲ *B. aspleniifolia*, blooming at Broken Bay, N.S.W. and Frazer Island, Qld. ▼

and more bushland is engulfed by suburban development around the populous city. It is a low, straggly shrub, rarely more than 3 or 4 feet high and often much lower, but the soft, lemon-yellow flower spikes, up to 5 inches long and 3 inches across, bloom profusely in winter. Many of these spikes contain only barren flowers, and when they eventually wither and fall they leave slim rods sheathed in rich brown plush; when fertile flowers are carried, rotund fruiting cones are formed, profuse with deeply embedded seed capsules like parallel rows of tiny mouths which open to reveal the black forked tongues of winged seeds. Coarsely toothed leaves, 2 to 4 inches long, are prominently veined on the undersurface and lined with soft white down. Leaf veins, branchlets, and young shoots are densely covered with short, matted, rusty red hairs (see picture back cover).

▲Developing flower-spike, *B. serrata*

▲ Leaves of *B. serrata*

▲ *B. serrata* before the golden styles are released

One of the largest and most widespread of the eastern species is the old man banksia, *B. serrata,* found on poor coastal soils from Tasmania to Queensland, hugging rocks on stony slopes and colonizing the hind dunes within sound of the sea. It grows as a tree up to 50 feet high, but in exposed situations is often dwarfed and mis-shapen. The gnarled and furrowed trunk and branches are frequently scarred by bushfires, and the bizarre hairy cobs with protuberant furry seed capsules are the banksia men of children's tales. Tough rigid leaves, up to 6 or 8 inches long and an inch or more broad, are dark glossy green; undersides are sometimes protected by a blanket of intertwined greyish or brownish hairs, sometimes almost hairless so that both surfaces are green. Margins are deeply saw-toothed, and an alternative common name, saw banksia, refers to this characteristic. On new growth the young foliage is copper-coloured, soft and woolly.

Flower spikes are large, sometimes 6 or more inches long and up to 3 inches in diameter. In bud they are silvery grey, soft and velvety to the touch. Later they bristle with the gold of fine, wiry styles; these are released from the bottom of the spike first and are finally straight. However, the petal-like perianth segments remain fused together for an unusually long time after the inflorescence attains full size, and during this period the blue-grey of the tepals predominates over the yellow of the captive styles. When the flowers wither, the styles turn orange-red and finally grey. Then the large, woody, velvet-clad seed capsules protrude at scattered intervals; changing in colour from coppery red to slaty grey, they remain tightly closed like heavy-lidded eyes, sleeping through several successive summers unless awakened by the scorch of passing bushfires. Shaggy old cobs, symmetrical, velvety budding spikes, grey-green, golden and burnt orange flowers, often occur together on the same plant.

▼ Stout, fire-blackened trunk of *B. serrata,* Myall Lakes, N.S.W.

◄ Fruiting cob of *B. serrata,* with seed capsules closed

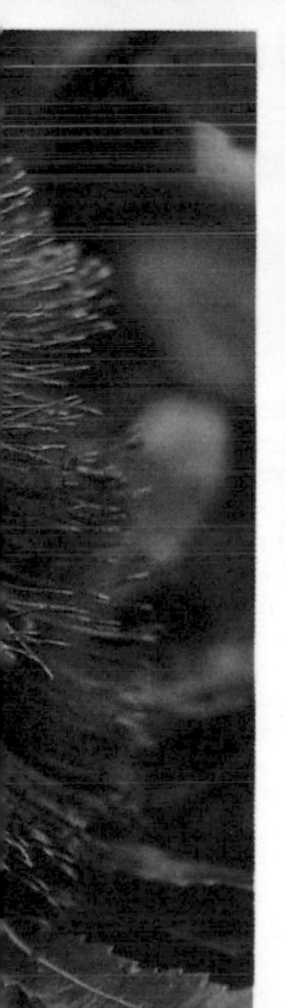

Banksia serrata

1. Styles are released from bottom of spike first
2. Cobs at all stages of development are on tree at same time
3. The spiralling rows of flowers can clearly be seen when the spike is in bud
4. Typical "banksia man" cob
5. Seed capsules opened by heat of passing bush-fire
6. New bark, exposed after fire-damage, is russet-orange

▼ Aborigines seek banksias for honey (*B. dentata,* Elcho Island, Arnhem Land)

Creeping banksia, *B. prostrata* ▲

Forty-odd *Banksia* species occur in Western Australia, and all are confined to that State except *B. dentata* in the north, which extends across tropical Australia to New Guinea. Of the remainder, the vast majority are found in the South West Province, that ancient corner of Australia which has remained segregated by sea and sand for countless millions of years, developing in isolation a unique and lovely flora. Many species and indeed some genera are entirely confined to the area, occurring nowhere else in the world. Of the 40 banksias found in this region, only two, *B. ashbyi* and *B. spaerocarpa* are recorded as extending beyond its limits, and then only into the sand-plains of the neighbouring Eremean Province.

Western banksias range from entirely prostrate shrubs such as *B. repens* and *B. prostrata,* which creep along underground with stems and even leaves often protectively buried beneath the surface of the southern sand-plains so that the flower spikes appear to be squatting directly on the soil, to *B. grandis,* which grows to 50 feet or more in the neighbouring coastal districts on the south-western tip of Australia, amid towering forests of giant jarrah and karri.

▲ Developing flower-spike of *B. grandis*, near Perth, August

▲ Fruiting cobs of *B. grandis* ▼

The dwarf or creeping banksia, *B. prostrata*, (pictured opposite) is confined to an area along the southern coast of Western Australia roughly extending from King George's Sound to the vicinity of Esperance, where the southern coastline curves north-east into the Great Australian Bight (the closely related *B. repens* has a similar range). Prostrate stems are covered with dense fur, and thick, flat, rigid leaves, often over a foot long, are carried erect on long stalks. They are very variable but are usually 1 to 1½ inches wide and divided almost to the midrib into broadly egg-shaped or triangular lobes. Flower-spikes, rarely above 3 inches long, are turned up at the end of branches and not closely surrounded by leaves. Soft grey in bud, they later turn cinnamon-red; the style remains curved but not hooked, and the stigma is tiny. When the fruiting cone develops, the velvety furred seed-capsules are prominent. *B. dentata* (lower picture, opposite) is a tropical species more closely linked with eastern banksias such as *B. marginata* and *B. integrifolia* than with the endemic banksias of the south-west. A small tree, 15 to 20 feet high, it grows across tropical north Australia and on the islands of the Gulf of Carpentaria. Banks and Solander collected the first specimens during their enforced stay at Endeavour River in north Queensland. Spikes are oblong or cylindrical, usually larger than those of *B. integrifolia*, but otherwise both flowers and fruit are very similar. Styles are about 1½ inches long, with small narrow stigma, and are finally straight. Flowers are yellow and are borne in winter. Leaves, up to 8 inches long and 2 inches broad, are irregularly toothed, with margins slightly recurved. The under-surface is not so white as in *B. integrifolia*, but the veins are more prominent.

The bull banksia, *B. grandis*, grows to 50 or more feet, forming a spectacular under-storey to the karri and jarrah forests of south-western Australia, and occurring in a stunted but profusely flowering form on the windswept hills overlooking the Southern Ocean. Enormous pale yellow flower-spikes, up to 18 inches long, are like great

candles in the tree; they bloom in spring and summer. Branches are woolly-coated, and the large, shining, dark green leaves, a foot or more long, are divided to the midrib into triangular lobes up to 2 inches in length and an inch or more broad at the base. Lower leaves are gradually smaller. Transverse veins are impressed above, prominent underneath; undersurfaces of the leaves are pale, and lined with soft, closely matted fur. The style of the flower is long and remains curved but not hooked; the stigma is small and oblong. Fruiting cones are large and spectacular.

The firewood banksia, *B. menziesii,* pictured on these pages, is closely allied to the eastern species, *B. serrata* and *B. serratifolia.* Leaves are flat or slightly wavy, with margins broadly and regularly saw-toothed; the style is finally straight and the long, prominently angled stigma is deeply furrowed. *B. menziesii* is a tree, up to 30 or 40 feet high and of rather straggling habit. Bark is pebbled, and branches thickly woolly. Leaves are 6 inches to a foot long

▲ Firewheel banksia, *B. menziesii,* in full bloom and in bud ▼

▼ Fruiting cob, *B. menziesii*

and up to an inch wide, with undersurfaces densely rusty-furred and marked by numerous parallel transverse veins. Flower-spikes are short and squat, rarely more than 4 or 5 inches long, and the silky, pink to rosy-red flowers bloom in autumn and early winter. As with the eastern relatives, flower-spikes in bud are silvery grey, soft and velvety; in bloom they remain rose pink or reddish while the looped tip of the wiry golden style remains firmly clasped between the perianth-lobes. These styles are released from the bottom of the spike first, and finally the flower cone is transformed to a golden fuzz. Seed capsules on the mature cob are scattered and very prominent. *B. menziesii* was first recorded by early botanist Robert Brown in the Swan River district near Perth. Its range extends northward to the Murchison River and the vicinity of Shark Bay, and inland across the sand-plains of the Avon district.

B. ilicifolia, the holly-leafed banksia, pictured opposite, is the odd man out in the genus. Flowers are carried in depressed globular heads instead of the typical cylindrical or oblong spike, and in appearance look rather more like those of *Dryandra* species than banksias. (*B. ilicifolia* however does not have the distinctive circlet of bracts around the flower-head, characteristic of dryandras.)

Holly-leafed banksia usually grows as a tree, 20 to 40 feet high, but sometimes remains shrubby and under 10 feet in height. Branches are woolly, sometimes even hairy, and bark of the trunk and main limbs is furrowed and corrugated. The holly-like leaves from which it derives its common name are dark glossy green, wavy-edged and irregularly prickly-toothed or lobed, up to 3 inches long and green on both surfaces; they surround the small, stalkless flower-heads in prickly rosettes. Flowers, yellow when first open, turn orange-red with age, giving the tree a two-toned effect; they open in August and bloom for many months. The fruiting cob is very small, and usually only one or two seed capsules develop. These are very prominent, almond-shaped, and coated with dense woolly fur. *B. ilicifolia* is found from the region of King George's Sound on the south coast to the Swan River district.

B. sceptrum, pictured overleaf, is a tall shrub or small tree, 10 to 15 feet high. Branches and leaves are densely furred, giving the foliage a blue-grey appearance. Leaves, 1½ to 3 inches long, are square-tipped, with scalloped margins, flat, rigid, and transversely veined. The flower-spike is thick and dense, oblong to cylindrical in shape and 6 to 8 inches long; yellow flowers are silken-haired and the floral

▲*B. menziesii,* with styles held captive and fully released ▼

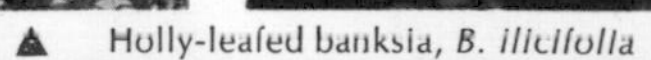

Holly-leafed banksia, *B. ilicifolia*

▲ B. pilostylis

▲ B. ashbyi, Carnarvon, W.A.

axis is clothed in the rusty red fur of velvety bracts. Curved styles protrude before the floral envelope opens. They are much longer than the flowers, and alternate with them in single rows. When set free, styles are finally straight; stigmas are large, thick and furrowed. Seed capsules are hairy, prominent and very thick. *B. sceptrum* occurs around the Murchison and Hutt Rivers in the botanical district of Irwin, on the central coast.

B. pilostylis (above) is a banksia of the coastal sand-plains around Esperance, near the Great Australian Bight. It grows as a shrub, 6 to 9 feet high, and in summer bears pale yellow to greenish flowers. Very narrow, sharply toothed leaves are up to a foot long, about twice the length of the flower-spikes.

B. ashbyi (above, right) usually occurs as a tall shrub or small tree, but may be stunted in growth and no more than 3 feet high. It is the typical banksia of the red sand country between Geraldton and Carnarvon. Flowers are bright orange, spikes squat and almost globular, 4 to 6 inches long and 3 to 4 inches in diameter. The spectacular long narrow leaves are deeply lobed, almost to the mid-rib. This banksia blooms in early spring; styles are finally straight.

▲ B. media

B. media (centre picture, right) is a compact bushy shrub or small tree, 10 to 15 feet high. It grows on sand-plain country around Esperance on the southern coast. Branches are densely covered with tiny hairs, giving the plant a hoary appearance. Leaves, 3 to 6 inches long and half an inch or so broad, are irregularly toothed or lobed along the margins and wedge-shaped at the apex. Golden flower-spikes are broad, up to 6 or more inches long, with the exposed tip of the floral axis sheathed with rusty red, softly hairy bracts. Fruiting cones have thick seed capsules almost completely submerged in the persistent remains of the withered flowers.

The round-fruit banksia (*B. spaerocarpa,* lower picture, right) is a shrub 3 or 4 feet high, widespread in the sandy heathlands of the south-west from Albany to Geraldton, and extending inland into the saltbush and mulga country of the Coolgardie district. Spikes are globular, or nearly so,

Round -fruit banksia, B. spaerocarpa ▶

▲Waratah or Albany banksia, *B. coccinea* ▼

mostly 2 or 3 inches in diameter but sometimes almost twice as large. Flowers are usually bronze-yellow (violet-tinged in var. *violacea*), and they may be seen in bloom all year round, though most profusely in summer. Styles are much longer than the flowers, and remain hooked, so that the inflorescence in full bloom looks like a golden pom-pom or exploding fireball on cracker night. The spherical fruiting cones are studded with rounded seed capsules, each marked with a prominent ridge along the suture, or else enveloped in a mat of interwoven withered styles, looking for all the world like a bird's nest. Branches are covered with minute grey-blue hairs, giving the bush a silvery sheen. Leaves are long and narrow, with margins tightly rolled back to the mid-rib and doubly grooved underneath. They vary in length from less than an inch to more than 3 inches.

The waratah banksia, *B. coccinea,* (also known as the scarlet banksia and the Albany banksia) is an erect, slender-branched shrub usually about 10 feet or less high but occasionally growing to 15 or even 20 feet under ideal conditions. Squat, almost globular flowerheads are about 2 inches in diameter. Flowers are carried in pairs in regular vertical (not spiralling) rows, with each pair overlapping the last rather like roofing tiles on a house. Perianths are softly furred, dove-grey, and the long styles are vivid scarlet, tipped with a golden stigma. Each pair of flowers in the regimented rows opens in such a way as to allow the curved styles to protrude in parallel pairs. The tips of the styles remain captive, prisoners of the perianth lobes, for a considerable time, so that the squat spikes are dramatically striped by double rows of silvery grey flowers alternating with double rows of arched, scarlet spines.

▲ Acorn or orange banksia, *B. prionotes* ▼

▼ Fruiting cob, *B. prionotes*

▲ *B. prionotes,* showing unusual leaves

When the styles are finally released they obscure the flowers and the spike becomes a spectacular brush of gold-tipped scarlet. After the fall of the withered flowers, the fruiting cone is more or less egg-shaped, and the seed capsules are very small and thin, scarcely protruding at all. Branches are densely coated with short, soft, matted fur, in which occasional long spreading hairs are often intermixed. The grey-green, rigid, leathery leaves are stalkless or almost so, oblong to rounded or heart-shaped, and bordered by small irregular prickly teeth. They are up to 3 inches long and are prominently veined underneath.

B. coccinea is common on the exposed coastal sand-plains around King Georges Sound and adjacent districts (hence the alternative common name, Albany banksia) and also occurs in the Porongorup and Stirling Ranges, blooming prolifically in moist gullies under the shelter of tall trees, each slender branch carrying its scarlet and grey spike. On the coast it flowers from winter to mid-summer, and in the mountains from late spring to autumn.

Featured on the front cover, and pictured on this and the previous page is the acorn or orange banksia, *B. prionotes*. This banksia grows as a tree, 20 to 30 feet high, on white sand in several districts of the south-western botanical province, ranging from King George's Sound in the south to the Murchison River north of Geraldton. Spikes are up to 6 inches long, and the bright orange prominent styles are released from the bottom first, contrasting sharply with the soft, silvery-white buds, giving the inflorescence its acorn-like appearance. The style is rigid, incurved at the base, then finally erect, with narrow furrowed stigma.

▼*B. prionotes*, photographed near Lancelin, W.A., in August ▲

B. prionotes in bud ▶

▲ Showy banksia, *B. speciosa*

Rounded seed capsules are prominent on the fruiting cones after the withered flowers have fallen. Bark of trunk and branches is ash-grey, softly and densely furred. Leaves are a foot or more long, half an inch to an inch broad, flat to undulate and regularly scalloped along the margins, each shallow lobe ending with a short rigid point. Numerous fine transverse veins, converging at the apex of each lobe, are clearly visible on the undersurface.

A spectacular western banksia of the sandy heathlands around Esperance is *B. speciosa,* known as the showy banksia. This tall spreading shrub has woolly white branches and remarkable leaves, 12 or more inches long and divided to the midrib into numerous triangular lobes, the larger ones three-quarters of an inch broad at the base and nearly as long; they diminish in size towards the end of the leaf. These elongated leaves are flat and rigid, furry white underneath and marked with numerous transverse converging veins. Broad, oblong flower-spikes, 5 inches or so long, bloom in January. Perianths are hairy and yellowish-green, and the erect, rigid styles are hairy also, incurved at the base; stigmas are furrowed. This banksia

▲Flowering spike and fruiting cone of *B. speciosa* ▼

▲ *B. attenuata* ▼

was first recorded at Lucky Bay by Robert Brown, the young Scottish botanist who accompanied Flinders in *Investigator* during 1801-2. Over a period of three and a half years, Brown collected and described almost 4000 species of Australian plants, the majority of them new to science.

Pictured on this page is *B. attenuata,* which has a wide distribution in the south west. It is a shrub or tree, 10 to 40 feet high, and bears bright masses of tall yellow spikes from spring to early autumn. Narrow leaves, 3 to 6 inches long, have margins evenly serrated and are usually white underneath, with prominent veins; they are flat, rather thick, and broader towards the base. Branches are downy. The cylindrical spikes are up to 8 inches long. Individual flowers are smooth, but the bracts which subtend them are densely hairy. Styles remain arched but not hooked, and the stigma is small and slender.

All banksias produce nectar in abundance, and many are valued honey plants. Nomadic Aborigines suck the blossoms to extract nectar, or steep spikes in water to make a honey drink. When the sweetly scented, honey-laden, sturdy spikes of *Banksia* are in bloom, birds, bees, insects and tiny marsupials abound. The insects push their way up the crowded rows, collecting nectar as they go from storage places at the base of each flower. Birds and pigmy possums find a foothold on the wiry arched styles, and probe for honey with furred tongues and long curved beaks or narrow snouts. Sometimes they seek instead the tiny insects which scurry deep among the spiralling rows of flowers; in either case, pollen is brushed off onto plumage or fur and transferred from flower to flower.

The most striking feature of *B. baxteri,* pictured on this page, is the leaves, which are divided to the midrib into sharp-pointed triangular segments, the larger ones being up to an inch long and three-quarters of an inch broad at the base. Globular flower-spikes are yellow, and bloom in late spring and summer. Individual flowers, bracts, and ends of branches bearing spikes, are covered with long fine feather-like hairs. Style is incurved at the base, thick, erect, densely hairy, and the stigma is narrow and furrowed. Seed capsules are very thick and prominent. This banksia grows as a tall, erect shrub, 6 to 10 feet high, and is common around King George's Sound and the flat sandy plains from the Stirling Ranges to the Pallinup River.

Banksias make attractive garden specimens and were popular overseas as early as the beginning of last century. Joseph Knight (*On Cultivation of Plants Belonging to the Natural Order Proteaceae,* published 1809) records the successful propagation of several eastern species. *B. spinulosa,* he writes, can be raised from seed, which should be sown without delay, or from well-ripened shoots cut at the node. Nowadays most gardeners prefer to propagate from seed, preferably sown in permanent positions, as many species resent transplanting. Fruiting cones should be gathered when the woody seed capsules are well developed and prominent. In most species (*B. integrifolia* is an exception) these are tightly sealed until severed from the parent plant, and may have to be forced open with a screwdriver, warmed in an oven to simulate the heat of bushfires, or left for some time in the sun. Spring is the best time to sow seed, in a mixture of sand, peat and leaf mould, covered lightly with bush soil (preferably gathered from their natural habitat). Banksias like a well-drained position, and most can stand plenty of water. As germination is unreliable, 2 to 4 seeds should be sown in each position, spaced a few inches apart, or else the whole cone can be partly buried, or placed between damp sacks until the valves open and the seeds germinate. If more than one germinates, the strongest can be selected. Growth is relatively slow. Some species flower on old wood, and should receive only light pruning.

▲*B. baxteri* ▼